Not the Breast Year Of My Life

Cara Sapida

Always On My Mind

Words and Music by Wayne Thompson, Mark James

and Johnny Christopher

To Greyson and Lilah, it's all for you.
To Lexi, and the ones who fought beside us.
And to Maggie, Thomas, Charlotte and Sophie's grand-
mother, we fight for you, too.

DEAR READER

The books started arriving at my doorstep days after I revealed my cancer diagnosis on social media. Breast cancer books, general cancer books, cancer cookbooks, self-help books, cancer workbooks, cancer coloring books, journals...forty-three books (a few of them duplicates) piled up on my dining room table.

One particular breast cancer book had been recommended to me by a friend so I picked it up, sat down on the floor, took a deep breath, and opened it. I didn't get past the second paragraph where I found mortality statistics—on the very first page. I slowly closed the book, lifted it up, and flung it into the wall.

That book is probably wonderful and helpful, and the author brilliant with good intentions, but I'll never know. My every thought was simply about my children.

My son, Greyson, was four and my daughter, Lilah, was just two years old. They were both too young to fully comprehend any of it. I tried my best to be honest, while shielding their young, innocent hearts from the ugliest sides of this disease.

My only plan was to fight and win, so I had no need for what I believed were outdated statistics.

Three people sent me the book *Dear Friend*, a collection of handwritten letters from breast cancer survivors. I opened this book next and after reading the first few letters, I took the book and clutched it to my chest. I held onto that book like I was hugging one of those brave women behind the writing. I thought of each woman taking the time to write down words of encouragement from where she now stood, after cancer. I'd never longed to be anywhere so much.

This stark contrast in books is something I thought about often while I was in active treatment. And while every woman facing a cancer diagnosis is different, I made a firm decision early on that I would not google. I did not google. Google gives statistics, but I didn't want to be a number. I was looking for something specific that I wasn't sure a search engine could find—*hope*.

Hope is elusive at the start of chemotherapy. I was desperately chasing it and discovered the single best method to ease anxiety and calm fears was found speaking to women on the other side of chemo. They were rocking their pixie cuts and returning to their lives. They were mothers who were back to normal routines with their kids.

I relied on these women who had just finished treatment, calling and texting them with questions day and night. I was grateful for their firsthand knowledge to light my path.

Even if you don't have a friend who has gone through breast cancer, you are not alone. Don't be afraid to reach out because the women in the breast cancer community embody the most supportive sisterhood. I finished active treatment in December of 2020, and I'm now the one answering questions from women newly diagnosed, women who are desperate for a connection to someone who can help it make sense.

This book is meant to be a supportive sister. I'm unable to give medical advice, but I hope to answer your other questions as you begin navigating all the emotions that come with a breast cancer diagnosis—your own or a loved one's.

For all the questions you don't know you have yet, or for those of you who just want to feel like someone knows what you're going through, this book is for you.

Writing gave me purpose through the pain, and this was more of a journal at the time. I've adapted those entries into chapters to help share my story with you, equipping you with an idea of what's to come and inspiring some hope.

Chemo is in my rearview mirror, and when I adjust the angle, I see wild, curly hair grazing my shoulders. I smile. Then I adjust my mirror some more and I see two smiling faces in my backseat—my children, now seven and five.

I fought my hardest for them.

You can do this.

CONTENTS

It Can Happen to You

As a television news reporter, there's one sentence I've heard a lot over the span of my career: "You just never think it can happen to you."

It started out as one of those beautifully promising mornings, where my outlook on life felt extra positive after a rough few months.

I actually found my lump that turned out to be breast cancer while doing a big, morning stretch. The kind of stretch that feels so good in every circumstance except when it leads you to cancer.

Discovering a lump on your own, outside of a gynecologist's office or even a monthly self-check, is startling. Your fingers stop. It's this split-second, frozen-in-time moment before the world starts turning again where subconsciously you're aware that life as you know it is about to change.

Maybe you held your breath. Maybe your ears were ringing. Maybe you felt pure disbelief. But I knew.

A young woman I follow on Instagram posted that she dropped her loofah in the shower and decided to wash her body with her hands. She credits it with helping to save her life, and now encourages women to "drop the loofah."

I had just joined a kickboxing gym and was in that good, pulled muscle stage. You know the stage where you're not limping but still feeling the burn of a gym newbie. Three weeks of intense punching and kicking had me feeling like maybe I was getting in shape. That morning I got out of the shower and thought, *Damn! Your legs look a bit strong!*

Those words of affirmation were rare for me because I had been busy beating myself up. It was the summer of 2020 and I had just made it through the most stressful spring of my life.

I wrapped my body and hair in towels and sat on my bed. I turned on the news to get the latest on this new COVID-19 global pandemic before my workday began. This "before" moment in time is burned in my brain, how casually I just got ready for work with no knowledge of a small, aggressive monster in my chest.

I reached my arms to the sky, leaned my body to the right to stretch the sore muscles. I rested my right hand under my armpit, and there it was.

My fingertips sought it out. They moved it around and without one doubt in the world, *I knew.*

My first thought was my children. *I have a two-year-old daughter and a four-year-old son who need their Mommy.* June 18, 2020 at 8:16 a.m., I texted my coworker:

> I just found a lump on my breast. Going to try and go to the gyno and get an ultrasound and not cry.

At the gynecologist's office that morning, the doctor felt my lump while I held my breath. She told me she wasn't overly concerned but would send me for an ultrasound just to be safe.

One of my best friends is an ultrasound technologist. She helped me get an appointment and did her best to talk me off the ledge. She has seen plenty of lumps that turned out to be benign, and plenty of women who left relieved. She also lost her beautiful mother to breast cancer.

Nervous and numb, I stripped down from the waist up for what would be the first of countless similar exams.

I later learned the radiologist examining my lump on the screen had just returned to work after fighting breast cancer. I watched her eyes like a hawk for any sign of what her medical training saw on the screen. And I watched as her eyes grew just the slightest bit wet.

Was it my imagination?

She told me we would need to do a biopsy.

The doctor's assistant, who had the bedside manner of a warm loving grandmother, pulled up a stool and clasped one of my hands into hers. She stayed beside me while the radiologist prepared for the biopsy. That same woman actually ended up sending two "Thinking of You" cards to my house during chemo.

I remember not speaking during the procedure. I remember my arm ached as I held it above my head for what felt like ages. I remember bracing for the loud sound they warned me about—the sound of tissue rocketing out of a tumor through a device. The shockingly loud noise startled me so much, words finally came to me. I whispered, "I have young children. They need me." A tear fell off the side of my nose.

You get sent home to wait for the results.

I remember every moment of that day and that drive, fear in my fists as I gripped the wheel. Every fiber in my body knew what was coming next, even while I desperately wished my instinct was wrong. That deeply powerful intuition has a track record of always being right.

My biopsy came back positive for breast cancer—an initial incorrect diagnosis of stage 0 triple-negative DCIS with *suspicion* of micro-invasion. Micro-invasion meaning perhaps a few cancerous cells snuck out of the tumor. My surgeon explained I'd need to undergo more testing to determine if it was invasive or non-invasive.

Even though I'm in my thirties, I did have a mammogram done in October the year before, and there wasn't anything concerning in my breasts. I had been experiencing an aching in my other armpit that was likely from breastfeeding.

In seven months, a two-centimeter cancerous tumor had formed.

At this stage, my children didn't know about the breast cancer. They only knew to be careful wrestling around Mommy because of my biopsy boo-boo. My breast had a deep blue and purple bruise where they'd removed that tissue. When we said prayers to God that night, my sweet son prayed for his magical Christmas elves to "heal Mommy's boo-boo on her boob before the morning." He talked about elves year-round in our house.

But when I woke up, the cancer was still there.

I just never thought it could happen to me.

The Diagnosis

The next few days I thrived with my stage 0 diagnosis. I felt some apprehension but was assured that this was manageable and probably would not involve chemotherapy.

We would need a lot more testing to determine if I had a genetic mutation. If I did, I'd need a double mastectomy. I was overwhelmed, but comfortably in management mode.

The main question plaguing my thoughts—*why me?*

I was healthy, mostly vegetarian, I exercised and used sunscreen, bought organic, limited processed foods, and breastfed my babies. I didn't eat candy, never put plastic in the microwave, steered clear of "diet" anything, and put toilet paper down in public restrooms. I went to bed at 9:30 p.m. most nights and drank filtered water.

How could I get cancer?!

I was in denial *because there had to be a mistake*.

A week later my surgeon called and told me the pathologist made a mistake.

"The pathologist read your report wrong," she said.

I'd been playing with my children when my cell rang. I'd probably been staring at the phone for days, willing it to ring, begging the universe to send good news.   I ran for refuge to take the call, and ended up alone in my son's bedroom, carefully closing the door behind me. I crawled onto his bed and curled into myself, rocking my body with my forehead resting on my knees. I was not prepared with a pen and paper, and I didn't even turn on the lights. But at the words "read your report wrong," I jumped off the bed, relief surging through my limbs.

I knew it! I knew there was a mistake! I knew it with every fiber of my being. This had been pretty brutal, thank you very much, but all will be well, this was just a simple mistake! I knew it.

Of course, I didn't say any of that aloud because I didn't have the time. I thought it all and more though, in that split second before she said, "You have stage II triple-negative IDC, which stands for invasive ductal carcinoma. It means the cancer has spread outside of your tumor."

I had been asking the wrong question...

Why not me?

Cancer does not discriminate. Cancer doesn't care if you have young children. Cancer doesn't care if you're a people pleaser and nice to everyone. Cancer for sure doesn't care that some health plans don't cover mammograms until the age of fifty. Cancer hasn't noticed the shocking number of young women getting diagnosed in their twenties and thirties. Cancer's probably just confused about the CDC's Breast Cancer Screening Guidelines for Women chart on their website.

I curled back up in my son's bed and listened to plans and next steps and knew I should have grabbed that pen and paper. The apprehension turned into fear pretty quickly. When I stood up I'd be entering enemy territory. I'd be forced to respond to an unprovoked sneak attack, and I was not prepared for battle.

There would be no turning back. I had to fight cancer.

Kick Me When I'm Down

Many women get their cancer diagnosis while going through another hardship. I've met women who were also taking care of an ailing loved one, had recently given birth or just lost their job. One young woman was living in NYC, alone, far from her loved ones and her landlord wanted to charge her an astronomical fee to break her lease to get home to family who could take care of her.

I was going through a separation.

Cancer during the earliest days of the COVID-19 pandemic, and through a divorce was a perfect storm of complete misery.

All marriages hit the occasional pothole, but a couple months before my diagnosis, mine had driven into a black hole without any chance of recovery. We were attempting and failing couple's therapy when an unexpected curve ball came called *the world shutting down*. Even therapists needed time to pivot and switch to virtual sessions, something that is now commonplace post-pandemic.

When the lockdown began and I was still living with my husband, we weren't exactly on speaking terms. He had been looking for a rental, but there were no rentals or real estate. And if I wanted a break, not a restaurant, bar, nail salon, movie theater or church in Western Pennsylvania was open. There was nowhere to go.

In the six weeks of separated-but-living-together that led right up to my diagnosis, my only escape was work. As a television news reporter for the NBC station in my hometown of Pittsburgh, I had a job that couldn't be performed in the safety of my home. We were tasked with hitting the eerily empty streets to cover the pandemic at a time when people were still searching for masks.

I get it, masks are everywhere now. I recently read an article that said a French geologist worried soon there will be more discarded masks in the *ocean* than *jellyfish*. But during this small window of time, right after the COVID-19 virus arrived, I felt pressure to find one.

I remember scouring my basement for an old package of large white masks that we'd purchased when I wanted to help paint our walls during pregnancy. My aunt sewed me a cloth mask.

Confusion about COVID-19 was swirling. Lines were forming. There were a growing number of people blaming the media, lumping national 24-7 network news media, social media commentators, and local news in one big group.

I remember watching my coworkers working to get facts, get answers, and get home safe to their families. Many of us were asking the questions to officials and passing along the answers, while the distrust continued to grow. While work was stressful, homelife was also stressful. With everything still shut down, work remained my only escape from the avalanche that was my marriage barreling toward divorce.

If my life were a story, right around the separates from husband chapter, the reader would never have imagined a cancer diagnosis coming. You never see the bus that hits you.

The day the governor announced gyms could reopen, I sprinted out of the house. I finally had an option that wasn't home or work. I signed up for a trial week at a kickboxing gym and quickly discovered this form of exercise was helpful for my mental health. You can picture any thing or any face on a punching bag. I joined the gym.

Before having children, I'd been a daily exerciser. But as a new mom, I hadn't made it a priority, simply unable to find the time. I'd work out occasionally— a yoga class here or there, a quick trip to the elliptical machine to barely break a sweat. I told myself I was *active*, because I was always chasing toddlers around.

A day late and a dollar short, I found myself prioritizing it. I was going to my new kickboxing gym to exercise every day, which is why I pulled those muscles.

If the world hadn't locked down, would I have joined a new gym? If I hadn't separated from my husband, would I have been searching for an escape? How many weeks would have passed before I discovered the lump in my breast that I just learned was the most aggressive form of breast cancer? Cancer kicked me when I was down, but maybe those hardships helped save me.

My new therapist at the Cancer Caring Center, Wendy, told me that I needed to find "strength in the struggle," and that which didn't serve me needed to be left behind.

"Just let it go," she said.

We talked extensively about the importance of managing stress in life and making it a top priority now and in the future to help prevent a breast cancer recurrence. Wendy encouraged me to work on stress management at a time when I was getting hit with some of life's top stressors simultaneously. No pressure! Stress-free may be an unrealistic longshot but managing unnecessary stress felt doable.

The saying "don't sweat the small stuff" is casually thrown around. But now reflecting on the "stuff" that caused anxiety and stress before cancer entered the chat, I realized it was all trivial. Health is what matters.

A cancer diagnosis will remind every one of us that this is not a practice life.

After my oncologist mapped out my chemotherapy game plan, my husband offered to cancel the rental he'd finally found and not move out. We both knew the next few months would be an uphill battle, without a lot of help because of the risks of getting COVID with a chemo-induced compromised immune system. I couldn't have friends and family in and out of my house. I knew I'd need all the help I could get. But I also knew the best decision for my family wasn't prolonging the inevitable divorce.

I did a lot of soul searching in a short amount of time and told him to book the U-Haul. While I greatly appreciated his offer, I had to let him go.

Sharing Your Story

Sharing your cancer diagnosis with loved ones is painful, bordering on impossible. We want to protect them from the news, and it's tough getting through the details without breaking down. I choked on the cruel words that had become my new story.

If you've ever received a phone call and the somber voice on the other end says, "I have something I need to tell you," you're automatically bracing for the worst news.

The irony here is that some people actually receive these worst-news calls and say with relief, "Whew! I was worried you were going to tell me you had *cancer*!"

They'll say something like, "Oh, you lost your job? That's awful, but I was really worried you were going to say you had cancer!"

Or you'll hear, "You're getting a divorce? Goodness, girl! I thought you were going to say you had cancer!"

Yet most of my friends learned of my breast cancer diagnosis in a social media post. I wish I could have told more people personally, but those conversations were grueling.

I had to FaceTime my closest friends and family to share my news. Some of them started crying before I finished the sentence. Some people wear their hearts on their sleeves; I wore my sorrow on my face.

My face said, *I'm so sorry for what I'm about to tell you. And this hurts me, but I also know it's going to hurt you, hurting for me.*

There are so many people to tell: your best friends, siblings, cousins, neighbors, colleagues, boss, kids' daycare, kids' teachers, high school friends, college friends, new adult friends, and the mailman. You might not have the emotional bandwidth to tell everyone on your list.

The definition of *emotional bandwidth* is the ability to know how you are honestly feeling in a given moment. It also includes accepting responsibility for your energy management, which is understanding the limit to the amount of information your system can handle.

In other words, we can only handle so much on a good day, typically juggling countless things. Do not feel guilty if you can't muster the strength to relive the diagnosis details time and time again.

If no one else tells you this today, know that sharing a cancer diagnosis takes a lot of energy and you get a pass—a Get Out of Telling Everyone Free card.

This deeply painful and personal diagnosis may devastate those around you, but it's yours. Protect yourself for as long as you need.

But I began to feel some pressure to share my diagnosis publicly.

As a television news reporter with a professional Facebook page that I updated regularly, it seemed like I had two options: Tell the viewers of my diagnosis, or disappear off both TV and social media for the next few months then suddenly return bald or in a wig. It didn't seem like much of a choice.

My immediate concerns were fear of sympathy, and fear of the *stories*. I knew right away I would hear heart-wrenching stories of lives lost to this awful disease. I didn't want stories to set me back.

There's a chapter missing from this book, and the only one that I never completed. It was titled "Sympathy versus Empathy," and while every other chapter came naturally to me, that one was a struggle. It's not easy to explain without fear of hurting feelings.

The truth is that almost everyone who will want to help you will struggle to find the right words. Sometimes I just wished they'd say, "Damn, that really fucking sucks. But I'm here if you need absolutely anything."

I recently picked up the breast cancer book *Please, Don't Send Me Flowers*.

I felt that. You can be wholeheartedly grateful for the flowers and still understand this sentiment. We tend to appreciate the support but dread the pity.

So twelve days after I felt that lump I sat down and did what felt natural: I began writing.

"Like many of you, I experienced this pandemic while going through some hardships, in my personal life as well as with my health."

I talked about the stretch that found the lump and how my children were my first thought.

"My children continued to be my main thought through the ultrasound, mammogram, biopsy, second mammogram and as I waited by the phone."

I talked about the phone call that I wouldn't wish upon anyone, where you learn you have breast cancer.

"I wish I could have told more people personally. I've learned sharing my story to loved ones is painful. It's emotionally draining. I want to protect them from this news and for days I couldn't get through the details without breaking down. But, for now, I'm all cried out and honestly feeling strong."

I wrote about my hope that by sharing my story maybe I'd reach a woman who needed to hear it.

"Maybe you're doing a self-check right now, or picking up the phone to schedule a mammogram in your 30's. Maybe

you're in the middle of a breast cancer journey right now and can relate. Let's be strong together."

I hadn't yet started to hate the word journey, but I would outgrow that word soon enough.

"Or maybe you're reading this and it's a reminder to treat one another gently. You never know the pain someone is living through—and how far it can go to offer some kindness or a bit of grace.

I read somewhere that cancer may have started the fight, but I will finish it. And I am here to fight.

All prayers and positive energy are greatly appreciated."

I proofread my words over and over. I anxiously hovered over the post button. I just had to launch it. I pulled the pin from the hand grenade, and there was no getting back from this moment.

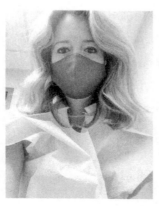

I posted my story to Facebook and Instagram with a photo I had taken sitting on my gynecologist's table. In the photo I'm wearing a white paper gown, looking down with sadness in my eyes, after I was told I should get an ultrasound "just to be safe." It's a photo that went directly to Melissa, my friend who is the ultrasound technologist.

I threw my phone onto the bed and walked away. If just one woman could be saved by sharing my story, I told myself it would be worth it. If just one woman picked up the phone and scheduled an appointment to check out a breast lump, it would be worth it. If just one woman who was also recently diagnosed with cancer felt less alone, I felt sure it was worth it.

Hours later I picked up my phone and found an inbox flooded with messages from women saying *they called and scheduled a mammogram that very day.*

A couple weeks later I received another round of messages, this time from women saying they needed biopsies. And then a final round after that from several women saying follow-up appointments were scheduled, cancer was found.

Love, support and prayers from around the world also started coming in. Women with my exact same diagnosis reached out. Women who were terrified of sharing their diagnosis told me they hadn't told anyone outside of their immediately family. Some wrote they finally took a tiny, brave step forward and found their voice.

A woman I went to high school with, who had fought cancer a few years earlier, also commented on the post. She had shared a quote with me that I think of often. This quote is so powerful, just reading it instantly gave me a boost of strength. I read it aloud:

"Fate whispers to the warrior, 'You cannot withstand the storm.' The warrior whispers back, 'I am the storm.'"

If you are afraid to share your story, that is understandable. You are not alone. But if you can find your voice to help others or to find connection, do it.

Tell a friend. Tell them all. You might help someone, but you also might find a tribe.

And quickly I would find out it's the tribe that helps you get through the storm.

THE CANCER MARATHON

When you're diagnosed with cancer, there is one saying you'll hear a lot: "Fighting cancer is not a sprint, it's a marathon."

I love the marathon analogy. I do.

But it felt like I was entered into this race against my will, with no training— and wearing a pair of flip flops.

Who the hell signed me up for this?!

I have never been a runner. In high school I came in last place during the Presidential Fitness Challenge run around the track. I tried to make myself feel better about it by pointing out that I came in first place in the sit-and-reach. But it turns out not a lot of people are impressed by sitting and reaching.

When I moved to Pittsburgh for my job at the local NBC affiliate, my coworkers asked me to do a marathon relay for the Liver Foundation. I tried desperately to get out of it after agreeing in a moment of stupidity. I told myself I'd train hard, forgetting that you cannot actually train unless you run.

I didn't train at all and showed up the morning of the race ready to push through it. I had heard stories of runners who complete the full 26.2 miles without ever training.

I had to run approximately 2.5 miles and made it about one mile before I switched over to brisk walking. I couldn't breathe. The playlist I'd spent hours perfecting to get me through this embarrassment wasn't helping. I ripped my headphones out of my ears and searched for a water table in the distance.

I cursed myself for signing up because my poor performance was certainly not going to help my team. And in that moment a little old lady with white hair came up beside me and smiled as she passed me by.

I'd guess she was in her seventies or early eighties, and I was impressed. *Ok, so she trained*, I thought. I started giving myself a pep talk and was going to pick up again any minute. And as I looked ahead, I realized this elderly woman who passed me by was running on what appeared to be a prosthetic leg.

An absolute inspiration placed before me.

I shoved my headphones back in and took off. I actually ran the rest of the way and crossed my relay finish line filled with pride. My mom was waiting for me and cheering like crazy. We hugged and walked to the car arm in arm, exuding so much pride and exhaustion that people yelling congratulations surely thought I'd just finished the full marathon.

And while I've done plenty of exercise since, including CrossFit, hot yoga, and kickboxing, I have *never* stepped foot in another race.

So no, I absolutely did not want to take part in this "cancer marathon."

But I understood that it was time to mentally prepare for a long few months of treatment, followed by another long period after surgery, and even years of healing.

And no, I absolutely was not prepared in any way for it. But just like the strong women who came before me, I vowed to finish this race.

Fighting-Ready

Three weeks after my biopsy came back confirming breast cancer, I started perusing that stack of books that arrived. I was in search of dietary advice or life advice or a miracle written in the fine print. I wasn't sure if I was searching or just keeping busy, but there I was back on the carpet surrounded by a sea of books.

I opened one up, and it said if you have to have chemo, you better be "fighting-ready."

What the hell did that mean?

We've already established I cannot run.

That was enough reading for the day because it was all I needed. I threw down the book and headed back to the gym. I hadn't been there since the morning I found my lump.

But since I read no further, it appeared to be up to me to figure out what it meant to be fighting-ready, and punching felt like a step in the right direction.

Chemotherapy would begin in just a few days, and exercising was one tangible thing I could do to prepare. I started kickboxing every day again. Remember when I told you punching bags meant picturing anything or any face? This time I was punching this stupid disease in its stupid face.

Things I said to my cancer as I punched, "You're the most aggressive? I'M THE MOST AGGRESSIVE!"

And it felt good. Sometimes I felt strong even as tears landed with my blows. Fear just simmered under the surface as I put on a brave face. Anger wanted to boil over as tried to accept my new reality as a cancer fighter. There never was going to be enough time to be fighting-ready because none of us are prepared for the sneak attack that is a cancer diagnosis.

Outside of the gym, I felt less strong. Just looking at my children was enough to break me some days. My son, Greyson, was turning five years old and my daughter, Lilah, was just two. How do you explain cancer to your babies?

Greyson's hugs and thoughtful words punched me straight in the chest.

One morning he offered to go to Target with me and get medicine to heal my boobs. Another day I was sitting on the kitchen floor, a place I found myself often. So overwhelmed with sadness, I'd just take a seat. Greyson found me there and went straight to the living room, managed to lift flowers off the fireplace mantle and bring them to me. Someone snapped a photo of this moment. It's not centered, and it's a bit blurry, but it captures a child's kind heart.

Why did I keep sitting on the ground? I was trying to find my footing. I was giving myself the grace to feel this pain. To plop right down and let the tears flow.

I allowed myself unlimited moments of fear and sadness, hoping when it was actually go-time, I'd be all cried out. My hope was to get to a place where I could set aside all the anger and all the fear and just accept this situation as an ugly chapter I was going to get through.

There's a popular saying in the breast cancer world: "fight like a girl." But as I woke up another day closer to my first chemo, cuddling my babies, I had other plans.

I was going to fight like a mother.

The Sweatshirt

A few years earlier, in my hometown of Pittsburgh, a morning anchor at the ABC affiliate, my station's competition, had announced on-air that she had breast cancer. It was January 2017, and I had an eighteen-month-old who wanted to watch *Mickey Mouse Clubhouse* every morning. If Mickey wasn't on the TV, we watched my own station's morning news. For a reason I will never understand, but think about often, that morning we had on my station's competition.

Kelly Frey delivered a devastating blow to her audience, saying that she had breast cancer. I remember sitting on the couch, my hand to my mouth. I remember her saying it was an aggressive form of cancer, but without knowing anything at all about the disease, didn't know she had triple-negative. If she mentioned it, it didn't register, as it wouldn't for most people who aren't intimately familiar with types of breast cancer.

After sharing my diagnosis, the calls and texts started coming in, but I was having a hard time speaking with people. I needed to speak to someone who had beaten triple-negative breast cancer, and I needed it now.

I asked a mutual friend for Kelly's phone number.

Kelly was both brutally honest and full of hope—which is exactly what you want from a survivor. She didn't sugarcoat anything. She was the first to tell me that chemo is "cumulative," and while I might feel very strong after the first few treatments, it would catch up with me.

And she told me when I met with my oncologist for the first time, to bring an oversized comfortable sweatshirt.

That first meeting with your oncologist is typically when you discuss your specific type of cancer and chemotherapy plan. At that point all you can think about is grabbing a life jacket, anything to hang on to as your world seemingly circles the drain.

Kelly said, "It's a cold and shivering that you just can't imagine until you are sitting there."

I went to Dick's Sporting Goods to purchase the most comfortable sweatshirt I could find. I scoured the different areas like I was a detective on the most serious mission. Truthfully, as I was just swimming to stay afloat, this gave me something to do. It was something small that I could control, so I threw myself into the trivial task and purchased a nice, cozy one.

One of my new friends from an online support group suggested taking a loved one to the first appointment who could take meticulous notes. All the information you receive in this one appointment is critical, and there's a strong possibility you'll forget most of it.

My friend Melissa, 9 months pregnant with twins, went to my appointment with me. She sat in a plastic chair, pen and notepad resting on her giant baby bump, as we waited to meet my oncologist. I sat on a hospital table naked except for a flimsy pink gown. The air conditioning vent was directly above my head, pumping arctic air on me like spray at a waterpark. I was already so nervous that my legs and stomach were vibrating. And I was freezing.

This first meeting is overwhelmingly hard. Everyone with cancer will experience it. I have a hunch it's one of the hardest for oncologists as well, breaking awful cancer details time and time again.

And I've learned how difficult this appointment is for mothers.

One survivor told me she brought in a framed photograph of her children to show the doctor. And another told me she broke down sobbing on that table, saying she gave birth to a baby girl just days ago.

In so many of our cases this is the first opportunity for us to tell our oncologist that *we have children at home*. We say this with hope in our hearts that they'll look at us and say, "Oh, well you have children at home? Okay, sorry, this was all a mistake!" Or more realistically, "It's going to be okay. You will beat this. You will be there for your children."

As painful as it is to admit this, we all know they cannot give us these reassurances. They can give us stats and the best medicine available but they cannot give us false hope.

As I sat there shaking, I spoke for the first time. I whispered, "I have young children at home. They are two and four years old."

My oncologist told me she hears that a lot.

I hung my head with the weight of all of our collective sadness to share that detail with our doctors.

And then we got right into specifics about chemotherapy, start dates, side effects, genetic testing and scheduling. My oncologist dedicated a day every week for research and was a wealth of knowledge about triple negative breast cancer. My head still hung as I tried to take it all in.

She told me about a new immunotherapy trial that was underway, and asked if I wanted to take part in it. Research nurses would track my vitals every week, and for years to come. I wouldn't know if I was receiving the placebo or the drug until the trial closed someday. She explained I'd have to stick pretty closely to the trial, following the same chemo regimen as all the participants in it.

I thought about all of the women who volunteered to be part of trials before me— trials that led to the chemotherapy regimens we have today.

She'd said I had a few days to think it over, but it was an easy decision.

"Sign me up."

Melissa audio recorded the meeting on her phone so she didn't miss any small detail. She would eventually prepare an email to send to my family so that everyone was on the same page about what steps were ahead. Thankfully, I had that email to refer to because aside from the immunotherapy trial details, I don't remember much of it.

I just sat there numb and cold, focused on how in the world I forgot the sweatshirt.

The Dark Days

There is a window of time after you're diagnosed with breast cancer but before your treatment starts that is remarkably difficult.

I refer to it as the Dark Days because it was when I was in my darkest place.

During the Dark Days, you're still clutching onto denial, and speaking your diagnosis into the universe feels like it will make it real. It will get real quickly when chemo begins, but you aren't there yet. Many women close off and simmer in fear-based silence.

Confusion is the cloud above you during this time, with more questions than answers. Most of us who don't have any loved ones or close friends who had fought this disease didn't even know there were different *types* of breast cancer.

My Dark Days were magnified by a semi-routine bone scan that lit up like the Fourth of July. I had just exited the full body scan machine, naïve and probably smiling politely, when the tech asked me if I had recently been in a "violent car crash." I had not.

She told me I had to go back into the machine for more scans. I hesitantly crawled back into the machine and lowered myself down. Slowly the scanning began again, moving over my body from head to toe, back and forth, hovering over certain areas that my fragile heart imagined were coated in cancer.

I whispered to anyone listening, "I have children."

Where earlier the techs were chatty, now they avoided eye contact.

After the re-scans, one of the techs told me to go back to the waiting room while the radiologist reviewed everything again and determined if I needed a third round. My legs felt like I had attached the little exercise weight cuffs, as I dragged myself down the hall. I bitterly wished I had just asked my mom or a friend to come with me, but I hadn't expected this latest curve ball. There wasn't a person waiting nearby to offer me a reassuring hug.

I found my voice and turned back around.

"Excuse me," I said as I approached the tech, deliberately making eye contact. "What did you mean earlier with the car accident comment?"

She told me nervously that a lot of areas lit up, like my body had trauma—not necessarily "cancer."

Grasping onto a shred of hope, I told her about kickboxing. I told her I had been punching and kicking, including kneeing the bags with all my strength, and whacking it with my shins. She was visibly elated to be thrown this bone.

"Yes! That is probably it," she said.

The radiologist did not need a third round, but simply said I'd need a PET scan, a more intensive full body scan that would determine if those areas were trauma, arthritis, or cancer. *Or maybe I swallowed some glow sticks?*

Back at home, I didn't eat and I didn't sleep. My legs vibrated against my will, physically shaking me to my core. My hands roamed my body, wondering which areas had betrayed me.

During the Dark Days, you'll get calls from your oncology nurse or "nurse navigator," and it feels like a rope being lowered down when you're stuck in the hole. A connection to the medical team and treatment headed your way.

The call came, and I was both dreading and eager to get this critical PET scan done. Except, she told me insurance denied it.

That was unexpected.

My nurse resubmitted, and the insurance company denied it again.

Excuse me? Did the insurance reviewer whose job it is to approve or deny this crucially needed procedure see any *tech notes*? I imagined the tech wrote something like: "Lady lit up like the Fourth of July."

I fought the claim denial. Fighting the insurance company was the first small blessing in disguise—it pulled me out of a state of pure sadness and transformed me into an angry, self-advocating patient.

My oncologist told me they would need to conduct a "peer-to-peer" review with the insurance company to fight for the test.

Chemo was set to start in a week, and I didn't even know if my breast cancer had spread to my bones. Again, insurance denied it.

I offered to pay out-of-pocket and discovered the average cost of a PET scan is $5,750, with some closer to $10,000. I was currently making $0. As a part-time news reporter, I didn't qualify for any paid medical leave.

This is what I was dealing with privately as my friends learned of my diagnosis and started reaching out. Wonderful friends sent cards and flowers, dropped off meals and gift baskets, and I didn't feel present for any of it. Their kindness is a blur while I was laser-focused on getting a scan.

I was in the limbo of the Dark Days and desperate to know if I was days away from fighting breast cancer, as planned, or bone cancer. Pulling the covers over my head,

I sobbed silently. I couldn't answer calls or texts from the fetal position.

I made telemarketing-level phone calls, advocating for myself and my scan every day. Finally, it was scheduled.

The day of the PET scan, I took a newly prescribed Ativan to help calm my fears. This tech handed me a huge "lemonade" with a "sugary substance" that lights up any cancer during the scan. Sounds delicious. It is not. I had to force down every nasty sugary sip.

The tech explained that this procedure will make you feel like you pee your pants when the injection begins.

I had never heard of anything like this! I couldn't even imagine it.

Would I be the only patient who manages to not feel like they peed their pants?

I had a strong feeling this was one bizarre side effect that I wasn't going to experience.

The nurse deployed the injection and a warm, watery sensation instantly hit me right in the crotch.

Guess not.

After, I headed home to crawl under the covers and pray.

Several days later I was reading the book *Dear Friend*, with the handwritten letters from other survivors, when my phone rang. I grabbed it and ran outside. I didn't want to be around the kids for this call.

The doctor said, "Your results are in. Scan is clear."

I clasped my stomach, bending into the pure relief that knocked me forward, my knees hitting the stone patio. Relief to be fighting breast cancer. Who would have ever thought I'd be happy to fight breast cancer just weeks ago?

I immediately recognized this as a blessing in disguise.

The original plan my oncologist gave me was now in play.

I stood up. And just like that, I found my way out of the dark.

THE PORT

B efore your first chemo, some women opt to have a port inserted in their chest.

Without the port, my oncologist explained, chemo will wreak havoc on your veins. The kind of destruction that is not fixable. And if your medical team hasn't mentioned this, you may need those veins someday. The port is temporary but not irreparable. Vein damage is permanent.

Discovering you need a medical device inserted into your chest is devastating for most of us. I dreaded having a visible reminder of cancer displayed on my body, because you can see it protruding like someone put a tiny box in there. But I knew it was a necessary evil.

The chemo port has a tube connected to it that attaches to a vein in your neck. Your oncology nurse inserts the needle directly into the port for chemo.

My port surgery was scheduled for the morning of my first chemo. That is one heck of a jam-packed day. Hard pass for me, please!

Like with the peeing my pants sensation, avoiding chemo nausea, and losing my hair, I wondered if I could be the one woman to get a port without having her chest cut open and a foreign objected placed inside.

The radiology nurse called me the day before surgery to ask if I wanted twilight anesthesia or no anesthesia.

I wanted not to have cancer, but that choice wasn't on the menu.

The anesthesia was a game-time decision for me, and I opted to go without it, mainly because I was trying to be a badass and also because I am a glutton for punishment.

My radiologist had incredible bedside manner, made me feel extremely comfortable, and even had music playing in the background. I remember thinking, *This is quite nice and I'm glad I'm not sleeping through it.* He said that if at any time I decided it was too much, they were ready to deliver anesthesia immediately.

I was thoroughly enjoying the music. I smiled at the nurses while trying to think of some positive affirmations.

Cara, you are strong. You are a badass. Those lidocaine needles in your neck and chest don't even know how fierce you are. Who needs anesthesia for this walk in the park? You got thi—oh lord, what was that? Oh my, what is happening?

Full blown panic set in lightning fast.

I said out loud, "No, no, no, no. I don't like this. Is that your finger in my jugular vein?"

I made it about a third of the way through the procedure before I was begging for anesthesia.

I later learned that intensely unpleasant feeling was simply the tube being inserted into my neck.

I told Lexi, my new "breastie" about it. She'd had her port put in the week before me, and I asked her if she had experienced the finger in the jugular.

My girl, Lexi, always bringing the humor to our painful days. She instantly said, "Yes! I wanted to say to the doctor, 'I mean, at least buy me dinner first.'"

"How Fast Can You Get Here?"

At my lowest point, the morning after the disastrous bone scan, my children saw me crying so hard that I couldn't stand up. My brain had been stuck on repeat, picturing all the glowing body parts that had betrayed me. It would be another week before I found out the scan was clear, and my mind was racing with fears. I started to sob and could not stop.

Call it a panic attack, if you will. Or maybe I'd been bottling up my fear and emotions since the day I found the lump, and there was bound to be a breaking point. But I was walking downstairs when the weight of this evil disease hit me, and the devastation came on so hard, I couldn't function.

I don't know how long I wept on my bottom step, but I know it was long enough for my four-year-old to color four drawings for me and place them one by one next to me on the floor. It was long enough for him to go upstairs into my bathroom closet and hoist a large three-drawer plastic medicine box, carry it downstairs and place it next to me on the floor.

My sweet boy, searching for any remedy to make Mommy feel better. And still I couldn't get up. I knew how this was affecting him, seeing his Mom crying on the ground, and it only made me cry harder. I was a mother...I did not want breast cancer...and I was terrified.

I've never found it easy to ask for help and found no exception during cancer treatment. I only asked twice—once was on this rock-bottom Dark Days breakdown. The other when I overdosed on medically prescribed marijuana and needed an ambulance. That was particularly humiliating.

Through my tears I found the strength to text my friend Tracy who lives at the top of my hill.

"I need help. How fast can you get here?"

She appeared almost instantly, like Mary Poppins, whisking through the door and corralling the kids into the kitchen for a snack and rushing back to hug me.

Cancer during COVID times meant everybody kept their distance. Tracy's hug ended up being one of the only adult hugs I received all through treatment. Tracy hugged me right there on the stairs for a long time. She hugged me and did not let go until I felt all cried out.

It's a sad memory and not one I'm particularly proud of. I didn't have time to prepare a YouTube Kids distraction. I didn't know my first panic attack was coming for me at the bottom of the stairs. It pains me to remember the drawings and the medicine box from my son, with his huge heart, not knowing at all how to help his mom.

I only had so much gas in the tank. Ugly, body-rocking cries felt like punching the accelerator with the needle nose diving toward E. Gas preservation was critical. I wiped my face, stood up tall and slipped back into mom mode.

I'm always looking for ways to help women in this breakdown space, when you feel lost and afraid. The key is to take one small step at a time because they will add up, and actually faster than you can imagine.

The more you research—*without googling your diagnosis*—the more you'll discover how far breast cancer treatments have come. I stopped constantly asking "why me?"

Instead I worked on feeling blessed to be getting treatment in 2020, after decades of research which had led to today's medical advancements. I felt grateful to be part of an immunotherapy trial that I believe is the future of cancer treatment. And I was profoundly grateful to the women who came before and did their own trials that led to the chemotherapy that would save my life.

If you're on the floor, or the bottom step, that's okay. Have the ugly cry. Let it all out. Give yourself the grace to mourn what was before, and what comes next. If you're crying in front of your children, know this: they will look back at their mama as a damn fighter.

You will push through the toughest days, gathering up your might and finding your strength. You'll find your feet and you'll rise.

I recently attended a Halloween party on my street, with all the neighbors, and approached Tracy to tell her I was writing a book. I said I hoped the book was raw and honest but also intended to include some levity and funny moments. She said, "I think maybe it's time I tell you something."

"Oh no. Tell me what?" I asked.

"Remember the day you texted me asking for help," she asked.

I practically shouted, "Yes! It's in the book!"

She said, "Well, funny thing. I looked to my husband and said 'she needs me' and immediately got up and ran to the car. I didn't know if you were bleeding. I remember thinking maybe something happened to your port and you might just be bleeding out. I threw the car in reverse and backed right into our garage door."

"No, you didn't!" I gasped, my hand flying to my mouth.

"Yes, so to answer your question, 'how fast can you get here?' Faster than my garage door can open."

Side Effects

The internet is full of inaccurate information and outdated statistics about breast cancer. Do not google your diagnosis.

DO NOT GOOGLE YOUR DIAGNOSIS.

While I never once googled mine, I did google this: "effects of chemotherapy." I had been curious and perused with hope.

I spent some time reading results of this one Google search about how chemo is "like the flu." I told friends and family with such confidence that it was going to be a lot like the flu. I pictured myself with aches, chills, sweating, blowing my nose, maybe drinking a little vegetable soup next to a vat of Vicks and box of Kleenex.

I can assure you that this, too, is a load of inaccurate bullshit from the internet.

It's okay to laugh about this now, but there wasn't an ounce of laughter when the real effects of chemo hit me. And while every woman reacts differently to different chemo drugs—some push through without many issues, others really struggle.

Many newly diagnosed women purchase books just to read about the side effects. I took side effects notes all through chemotherapy, just to do my best to both warn and reassure the women diagnosed after me of what's to come.

A friend of mine from high school, Melyssa, is one of the women who scheduled a mammogram after my public post. She was also then diagnosed with triple-negative breast cancer. And she handled chemo like an absolute slayer. It didn't break her stride, only feeling a little run down in the days after an infusion.

Every experience is unique; I can really only share my own. But for the overwhelming majority of women who have experienced chemo, I can confidently say there will be good days where you feel well, and days when you do not.

The chemo game plan my oncologist explained to me while I shivered uncontrollably:

Round 1: 12 weeks in a row of Taxol, plus Carboplatin, more commonly known as Carbo, every third week.

Glorious 3-week chemo break.

Round 2: 8 weeks Adriamycin and Cytoxan, more commonly known as A/C, every other week.

Here's a brief overview before I get into the nitty gritty. On my weeks of only Taxol, I skipped into chemo with a smile on my face. I kept the mentality that this chemo was killing my tumor, and I welcomed it. Steroids administered with the Taxol gave me a couple days of intense energy, followed by a couple days feeling tired. The most difficult side effects were a foggy brain and completely wiped out short-term memory.

The mailman, God bless him, was still delivering daily packages from friends and family—and little did I know my brain wouldn't let me remember who sent *any of it*. No one warned me. It reminds me of that Adam Sandler movie when his girlfriend is breaking up with him and he shouts, "Once again, things that could've been brought to my attention *YESTERDAY*!"

No one told me my memory would disappear.

And those were the good days.

On my weeks of Carbo, I woke up with dread in my stomach and fear in my bones. I called Carbo my "hard chemo" and used the word "hard" loosely when I meant, that shit sent me to the ER three times.

Carbo felt like a mix of the world's worst nausea paired with a side of fire in my chest that shot out like a vicious fireball when I tried to talk or take a sip of water. Top that off with a hit of total exhaustion, and I wasn't a really big fan. It was a garbage can of malaise. And none of the prescribed medications took the edge off.

Lastly, there was A/C, which turned out to be harder for me than Carbo. There is much debate in the breast cancer social media groups about which of those two drugs are worse. I could detail the gagging, the crying, the clawing at the pillows, but I won't.

Instead, I can only share my hope with you that "this too shall pass." And I'll even admit if you would have told me that while I was suffering through it, I might want to punch you.

But almost all hard days are followed by decent days and even a few strong days. Focus on getting through that hour. Try to find the distractions to make it through the day. Think of each week as another milestone you're checking off.

It's not easy and no one can truly relate if they haven't experienced this process that is both emotionally and physically hard as hell. Lean on the women who have been there before and hold onto the faith that you'll blink and it will be behind you.

And do not google.

CHEMO NUMBER ONE

The day before I was set to begin Chemo, I reached out to all my new breast cancer connections asking for last-minute advice. I was waiting for just one of them to tell me it's just like the flu!

Feeling brave and bold to finally face the storm, I headed to the cancer center almost eager to get going. For weeks I knew this small lump was waging war, and it was time to fight back.

I learned that each week I'd be taken to a recliner chair, which I called the "The Chair", and I'd be assigned a nurse who would administer pre-meds and the drugs.

All my mental preparations didn't prepare me for how the pre-meds, medicine given to *help* you handle chemotherapy, would send me spiraling.

Still all smiles and positivity, I did warn the nurses that I don't handle Benadryl well before 50mg of it shot into my IV. The syringe was probably still mid-air when my reaction hit. It's the only time in all my days inside the cancer center that I raised my voice or wasn't in control.

This all happened so fast.

I started crying. Then my cries turned to *wails*. The Benadryl made me feel crazy, with instant restlessness, dizziness, and a pounding heart.

The truth that I had swallowed in the weeks leading up to that moment came tumbling out of my mouth in hard heaves.

I screamed, "I don't want breast cancer! I don't want to do this! I don't want to be here! Please! Please don't let me have breast cancer. Please, I am a mother. My babies need me. Please just let me go home to my babies."

After my diagnosis, during the Dark Days, my legs took on a life of their own. They would vibrate uncontrollably. It's one of the reasons my doctor wrote me a script for Xanax. I needed help controlling my vibrating legs.

During the Benadryl breakdown, my legs started to shake. My estranged husband was in the waiting room. My girlfriend Kara, who was by my side, went to get him. While it was the only time he came to one of my chemotherapy treatments, it was helpful that he had been there. Both of them held down my legs and the nurses took a step back, and everyone let me cry it out.

Finally my pounding heart began beating normally again, and it was time to start the treatment. I imagined the chemotherapy drug was going to hurt. I didn't know how it would hurt, though I envisioned myriad awful scenarios from a burning sensation to a feeling of psychosis.

But as the drip began, there was no sensation at all. I discovered the process of receiving an infusion was pain-free, and I found some comfort in that. I still didn't know what the side effects *at home* would be, but I was immensely relieved to find this step was manageable.

For the first time I discovered I could have extremely hard moments—and then I could press on. The only way out of this was forward. The only option I had was to start that drip.

It was the last day I received Benadryl in my IV. My oncologist cut the dose in half and prescribed me a pill to take orally. I'll never forget the tears I shed that day, despite feeling like it was an out-of-body experience. It wasn't. Benadryl was just the bridge between my mind and body that didn't care who was watching. I didn't care if the whole cancer center, or the whole world, heard me scream. I didn't want breast cancer.

I looked up at the Taxol bag, and followed the medicine as it dripped into my body. I felt in control. I could do this. I would do this. And then the Benadryl knocked me out.

Chemo Number Two

One week later, I was heading back to the cancer center for my second round of chemotherapy. I plopped down in "The Chair" with a smile on my face. I was polite as I thanked the nurse for my pre-meds. We laughed as I joked about chucking the Benadryl pill over my shoulder, or into the garbage.

Earlier that morning I had rubbed a thick glob of numbing cream on my port. I drank fresh juice. I had my coffee in a to-go cup. I loaded up my gray chemo backpack with a hardback copy of Glennon Doyle's *Untamed*, which ended up coming with me to every chemo because I cherished it and repeatedly quoted: "We can do hard things."

I also tightly wrapped up and shoved in both an electric blanket and a personalized blanket with photos of my kids that my cousin had specially made for these hospital trips.

The one question I've received more than any other since my diagnosis—by a long shot—is what can I get my friend who was just diagnosed with breast cancer?

1. Anything that's not a pink tchotchke purchased from some company capitalizing off this awful disease

2. A small electric blanket because it is cold in the chemo chair

3. A personalized photo blanket because it is cold and lonely, even with a loved one by your side

I grabbed my ice gloves from the fridge and packed them in my daughter's bottle bag cooler I'd used for daycare just one year before. Taxol can cause neuropathy in your fingers and toes. Some women opt to wear ice gloves on their hands and feet in an effort to prevent it. It's not pleasant, but it's doable. I did it for every treatment and didn't experience any neuropathy. And when my treatment ended, I dropped off the gloves to a new triple-negative fighting friend who was starting her treatment.

That morning, I gave hugs and kisses to the kids and told them Mommy had to go to the hospital, again, to get another shot. But I was strong and brave and would be back in a few hours. Then I skipped out the door.

The nurse took the bandage off my port, nice and numbed up now. I may have been a little overeager because I turned my head just in time to see a needle the size of a *nail* enter my chest. The kind of nail thick enough to hang heavy artwork.

You know the nail.

Was it really that big? I'll never know because I never looked again.

But that day, I didn't flinch. Without realizing it, I had been slowly crawling out of the Dark Days. I hadn't yet entered light at the end of the tunnel territory, but suddenly I wanted the chemo. I wanted all the poisonous, tumor-demolishing drugs in my cancer center's arsenal. Hell, bring out the nukes.

Did that nail needle haunt my Benadryl-laced dreams? A little. But I didn't let it frighten me or set me back. I noticed myself gathering strength. This was the beginning of feeling a tiny bit like a warrior. Harder days were coming, of that I was sure.

Maybe if I continue to gather up that strength, I could be the fighter they are calling me.

Maybe I didn't have to just *tell* my children I was brave and strong. Maybe I was.

I had a lot to figure out, but I did know for certain just one thing: how strong you can be when it's your only option.

The Hair Loss

A few weeks out of the Dark Days, I was trying to find my footing, when one morning I picked up my black and red bottle of heat protectant hair spray and hurled it straight into the trash.

I knew my hair days were numbered. I was trying not to obsess over it, but it was constantly on my mind. I grabbed my curling iron and set it to the hottest level. I planned to fry the hell out of my hair without an ounce of protection because I was a breast cancer rebel, and that shit was falling out anyway.

My friend Kelly, the morning anchor for the ABC station in Pittsburgh, and fellow triple-negative breast cancer survivor, said her hair started falling out fourteen days after her first treatment.

Would I be the one woman going through my treatment plan who didn't lose her hair? No, I wouldn't. About eight days after my first chemo I pulled the burning hot flat iron slowly through my dry, unprotected hair and listened to a satisfying sizzle.

I had no control here and every day that my hair shed more, my anxiety grew as well. The inevitable head buzz was coming.

Each morning I woke to find my pillow coated with hair. My son, who was used to having a "job" each morning in his pre-K class, asked if he could be in charge of hair removal with the lint roller. As soon as he woke in the morning, he'd run in my bedroom armed with the roller, on a mission. I'd laugh and say, "Let's do this!"

He'd crawl into my bed, and like a tiny archaeologist with a magnifying glass, he meticulously scoured the pillow. It became a point of pride for him to see each sticky sheet of tape covered in mom's hair. But our days of playing this game were coming to an end.

I avoided washing my hair for longer than I care to admit, for fear it would all swirl straight down the drain. Life before cancer, I wasn't one of those women who could get by on dry shampoo. When day three came, I always needed to scrub my scalp. This stand-off with the shower was doomed.

I precariously stepped into the shower, tilted my head back into the spray and held my breath. I checked the drain. All clear. I carefully placed the shampoo onto my head and with the tips of my fingers gently rubbed it in. Quick drain-check again. All clear.

Maybe my day's allotment of lost hair was left on the pillow?

I leaned back again to rinse, massaging my fingers into my scalp and the hair just came away. It snaked around my fingers, it puddled into my palm. I looked down at fistfuls of hair. Desperately I scraped at my fingers to dislodge strands and send them down the drain. We would need Drano, no doubt.

There was still shampoo in my hair. I tried again to carefully wash the rest of it out. My fingers splayed and my arms vibrated as I slowly pulled my hands away, long strands of hair coming with them. Hair slithered down my forearms, falling away at the elbows. I let the shampoo remain, sat down in the tub, and cried.

Screw conditioner. I was done here.

Stepping out of the shower I expected to look in the mirror and see a bald head staring back. Surprisingly, that was not the case. I looked the same.

How many showers did I have left before the hair was gone? How many depressing shampoos could I handle?

A couple days later my Aunt Darcie stopped by to visit. Darcie was a retired hair stylist. I handed her a pair of kitchen scissors, the kind that cut food and sliced bags open. Nothing was planned, I hadn't known it would be the day; it wasn't penciled into my calendar. The urge came out of nowhere, and I said, "Please chop it short."

Maybe you don't know this fun fact about hair stylists, but most would sooner chop off their own fingers than give someone a haircut with scissors suitable for trimming chicken fat.

She offered to drive home, two hours round trip, to get her scissors. I said no, these would work just fine. She offered to run to Walmart and get any thin pair they sold. I looked her in her eyes and said, "Please do this for me now before I change my mind."

So, on day sixteen, with my children by my side, my aunt cut my long blond hair into a choppy bob. She let my son cut a big lock, which I caught on video. We were all smiles as the hair landed in giant piles on my kitchen floor.

I hadn't had a super short haircut since sixth grade, and it surprised me how much I liked it. I decided I was not going to cry. Instead I was determined this cut would become something to look forward to. I was waiting for my post-chemo pixie.

THE BALD HEAD

It doesn't matter how strong you feel, how much energy you have or how determined your will is to fight like a mother, on my chemo regimen you are still going to lose your hair.

I've heard from a few women who say they chose not to talk to their children about any cancer specifics. It's a personal decision, but I was preparing to be bald and sick and occasionally bedridden, and I wanted my kids to understand what was going on.

Talking about boobs in my house wasn't uncomfortable or uncommon, because I had nursed my daughter just a year before this.

I told my kids that Mommy's boobs were sick and doctors were making them all better. And that was always the extent of it. If I was tired it was always because the medicine to heal Mommy's boobs made me tired. If I threw up—and I did a few times despite modern medicine making chemo more tolerable—it was because the medicine to fix my boobs made my belly hurt.

But I had real fear that my children would not handle their mom suddenly losing all the hair on her head.

What if they cried?

Then their bald mom would comfort them.

What if they ran away?

Then their bald mom would go find them.

I didn't see any way around this scenario, other than just being honest and praying for the best.

A couple days after Greyson's fifth birthday, I asked him to come outside with me to talk. My daughter was just too young to understand, but I knew sharing this with my son would help him process it better in the coming days.

We sat down on the stoop together, and I said, "You know how Mommy's boobs are sick? Well, the medicine I'm taking does something *crazy*. It makes all my hair fall out!"

And he said, "That sounds silly! Are you going to look silly!?"

I said, "Yes! I'm going to look *so* silly!"

We laughed and laughed as my heart ached and I swallowed through the growing lump in my throat.

I took his hand and laced his fingers in mine. He still had his toddler hands. I wanted to squeeze and kiss and hold his beautiful, little chubby hand and never let go. I wanted to freeze this moment, hit rewind and go back in time. I was desperate to get a do-over and find the lump before it was big enough for chemo, and forced me to have this conversation, face this outrageous mountain that is a breast cancer diagnosis.

He leaned forward on the stoop to get a better look at me. I remember thinking, *He's trying to picture me bald.* I knew the feeling; I couldn't quite picture it either. And he said, "Even if you look silly, I'm still going to tell you 'you look beautiful.'"

Lord, thank you for this sweet child.

If my son could tell me that, then the least I could do was tell it to myself.

The next morning, I knew it was time to shave my head. I had hoped my new, cute bob haircut would last weeks. I assumed taking the heavy weight of all that hair away would preserve it on my head. And I was wrong. Every morning my pillow, shoulders, back, and bed were still *covered* in hair. The lint roller was outmatched.

I called my local barber shop and asked if I could come in for a buzz. I didn't know the correct terminology. A buzz cut? A head shave? Gimme the chemo clippers.

I had dreaded this moment, and I felt *bitter*, like I'd boarded a full-speed treadmill against my will.

Anyone gonna let me off the cancer treadmill!?
No, okay cool.

Next stop is the hair?!

Awesome. Is there an emergency button to turn this whole thing off?

Jeff, a local barber who had given my son his first big-boy cut the year before, said he would make a house call. My house! His kindness and generosity during a pandemic was incredible. I felt so grateful that he could do this for me and later learned his grandmother, whom he called his best friend, was a two-time breast cancer survivor.

We prepared the back patio with a chair, front and center, so the kids could watch. I waited for Jeff to arrive that morning, feeling a sense of calm that I had not felt since my diagnosis. When I had imagined this day, I pictured myself being rock-bottom devastated. It was going to be hard to shave the sides of my head while I was sobbing in the fetal position.

But I discovered that wasn't the case. It was like I was a practicing Buddhist and had prepared for this moment my whole life. I was ready to be a breast cancer survivor, and I wasn't going to get there with a head full of hair.

I wasn't going to get there any way but going through it. I had to run and complete this gauntlet, and the big buzz was one of the harder hurdles.

The hair had to go.

Jeff turned on the clippers, grazing them over my head and my cousin, Audra, and girlfriend, Kara, started to cry. I closed my eyes. Breast cancer is hard on us and sometimes even harder on the people who love us.

Someone whispered that my head was a really lovely shape. I smiled and kept my eyes closed. Then Jeff let my son help him buzz a little, and Greyson did it carefully and took the job very seriously. Lilah, just two years old, unexpectedly took my hand. So I opened my eyes to be more present for her. We held hands while all the hair that remained landed on the stone patio.

I didn't want to see a mirror, but some photos were taken. I glanced at them but looked away. I still don't love the photos from that day.

My cousin Audra asked if I wanted a glass of wine, and I emphatically said *yes*. It would be the only glass of wine I had from July until October, when I was able to drink another glass during that "three-week 'vacation' from chemo."

We clinked our glasses to something I can't remember, probably "to being a warrior" or some sentiment that hardly resonated in the moment. Or ever.

I used to practice yoga regularly. Yoga instructors teach something called *drishti*, the science of eye focus. The goal is to relax and *unfocus* your eyes. It's supposed to help you with balance and deepen the meditation. I often struggled with this because my curious nature preferred to look all around the studio.

Post–buzz cut everyone was bustling around me to clean up the hair, thank the barber, and drink the wine as I sat there with my eyes unfocused.

My children came to the rescue, snapping me out of this daze. Crawling on my lap they both gave me big hugs.

Lilah told me she really liked my new hair, and it looked nice "like a hamster."

From the mouths of babes! My children weren't scared. They didn't run or cry. They loved me no matter how much I resembled a hamster.

Only then did the tears finally come. I hugged them tight. I could do this, for them.

Greyson got down and took a few steps away before smiling up at me. With gut-wrenching sincerity, he paused and said, "You still look beautiful."

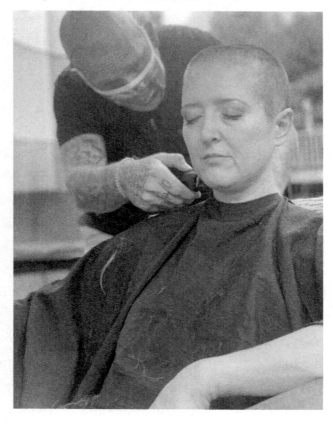

THE WIG

Waking up the next day, there was a brief, peaceful moment in time before I remembered my new reality. Grief, I'd only begun to learn, can be so startling in the morning, it feels like an ambush.

Whether you call this a fight, a battle, a journey, a marathon, an unfortunate life obstacle, a health setback—or whatever feels right to you— the part of this *experience* where you lose the hair is harrowing. It's broadcasting to the world that we are sick. It's broadcasting what we may have been hiding well, but can no longer deny to anyone, including ourselves.

That morning, I caught my reflection in the bathroom mirror and startled myself. I thought I was looking at Alpha, the whispering villain from season nine of *The Walking Dead*.

Someone on my medical team, somewhere along the way had explained that our hair falls out because the chemo is rapidly annihilating dividing cells—the healthy ones responsible for normal hair growth and the cancerous ones in a breast tumor. It's part of making forward progress. And it's temporary.

I tried on one of the new soft, cotton beanies that friends had sent me in anticipation of this day. It felt surprisingly good, tight and comforting on my head. And then I did what my friend Lexi had said she did the day after losing all her hair, I went downstairs and made my children breakfast.

I was so grateful to have Lexi, my first "breastie". Lexi was exactly one week ahead of me in her diagnosis and treatment, and she wasn't letting any surprises catch me off guard. She mapped the way for me, sharing the small wins and great losses from three states away in Indiana.

A week before, she'd Facetimed me after her ugly shower cry, after her hair came out in giant clumps.

And a week later, like clockwork, she text me a photo, showing off her new wig. She had a headband across her forehead holding the blonde hair in place. It looked 70's stylish. She looked so chic, right out of Hollywood.

With no hair left on my head, the pillow or in the shower drain, it seemed like a good time to go wig shopping.

I learned there are both synthetic wigs and human hair wigs, and different types of caps underneath to make them more comfortable on a completely bald head.

It was a fun experience, trying on these gorgeous heads of hair. I considered a fiery redhead wig, an Elsa blonde with waves upon waves, and a long straight midnight black. I lined them up on the counter to try on. The price tag on human hair wigs is not for the faint of heart. This was an investment, and I needed to be sure it was what I wanted.

I carefully bent forward, placing the first wig against my forehead like the salesperson showed me, and securing it against my head on the sides and back. I lifted my head, repeatedly flinging the hair back for each wig's big reveal. I liked them all! For a brief, light-hearted moment, I could almost pretend this was a dress-up game or finding the perfect wig for my Halloween costume. I still had these moments where I couldn't believe this was my new reality.

She handed me a blondish-brown wig that looked very similar to the hairstyle I'd had just weeks before. It was old Cara's hair only more voluptuous. It was gorgeous. And it was more expensive than the others. This time when I flipped the wig back, looking into the mirror, I briefly felt whole again.

"I'll take it," I said.

My daughter loved the wig, petting the long hair and telling me it looked so pretty. And while I never regretted the investment, I did surprise myself with the number of times I wore it, especially during active treatment. Only a handful. I felt most comfortable wearing a soft cotton beanie.

But the next day, I got dolled up, secured my new wig in place and headed out to run errands. I caught glimpses of myself in the rearview mirror and it looked lovely. I tucked it behind my ear and flipped it over my shoulder like a shampoo commerical. But after parking my car, I sat there for a long time. Something felt off.

In that moment, I didn't want to conceal evidence that I was fighting cancer. I didn't care if people did a double take when they saw me. Perhaps wearing the wig would feel better after all chemo treatments finally ended, when my hair would begin to grow back, and I'd want to accelerate that painstakingly slow process.

I felt inauthentic. What if I passed another cancer fighter in the produce aisle and they had no idea we had this connection in common? Misery doesn't love company, it craves compassion. It seeks encouragement and moral support. At the very least, we'd smile knowingly at each other, and I didn't want to miss that opportunity if it presented itself.

I pulled the wig off my head and draped it over the passenger seat's headrest. In a few weeks I'd have a little break from chemo, and already had plans to go to dinner with one of my best friends from childhood. I was already dreaming of sitting at the dinner table across from her, ordering food all casually normal, so far from my current reality. I knew I'd be grateful to have this beautiful wig help me to escape reality for a bit. And on that day, I'd come to find out that taking the wig off at the end of the night was pure relief, similar to a bra coming off after work.

But on this day, I needed to be in the moment.

I left the wig in the car and headed toward the grocery store. This time I caught my reflection in the front window and made eye contact. Even if I ran into no other cancer fighters, I saw myself.

You got this, Alpha.

THE NAUSEA

Determined to put up a valiant fight, those first few weeks of chemo I mustered the kind of strength that catapulted me out of bed hours before the kids stirred. I sat on my kitchen floor and chugged green juice, freshly made the night before.

A couple hours later I blended a vegan organic protein shake, chugged that, played, taught, and wrestled with my kids all day. I murmured to myself the ever inspirational, "I got this."

Until I didn't.

The two thoughts I had right after being diagnosed:

1. I have young children.

2. I'm not going to handle the nausea well.

My chemo was always on a Tuesday and thanks to the simultaneous administration of intense steroids, Wednesday was typically an easy day. The steroids made me feel invincible for a short time. They'd slowly wear off and I'd be a bit tired, but nothing I couldn't handle.

My nurse, Roseann, warned me it could be a *very* different story after my first Carbo treatment. Carbo is a common and vicious drug for women with my BRCA1 genetic mutation. Roseann suggested I be proactive by chugging as much water as possible to flush the chemo drugs from my body and begin taking anti-nausea drugs on Thursday night in preparation for the steroids to wear off by Friday. Unfortunately, by Wednesday afternoon, I was hit in the face with a brick of nausea.

I mean blindsided.

I am no stranger to morning sickness. With both of my pregnancies I vomited quite a bit. I threw up twice on my own lap driving home from work when I was pregnant with my son. I threw up bright red Gatorade in a snow pile on the side of the highway next to my news van in such a projectile fashion that it looked like I left behind a crime scene. I daydreamed about crumbling up saltine crackers and throwing them at people who suggested I nibble on one before getting out of bed in the morning. That would do the trick.

This was no morning sickness.

I felt the nausea in the pit of my stomach and a heat in my chest and throat. The intense heat didn't feel like heartburn, but as if I had swallowed a hot towel. I'd been told anti-nausea medicine has advanced to the point that it's rare for chemo treatments to trigger violent reactions as it's often portrayed in the movies. I had high hopes that this would be the case. But every Carbo week, I found my bald head back in the toilet bowl.

The problem here is two-fold: nausea doesn't begin to ease up until the chemo drugs are flushed from the body, but medicines created to help ease the nausea are constipating.

You can't properly flush the drugs if you're constipated. I tried to help my body by drinking more water, but my throat wouldn't cooperate. I'd tilt the water bottle back, and my throat would close right up.

Years ago, I had a friend who said his mother's claim to fame in their family was the phrase "water makes me gag."

I laughed and laughed at this! I'm a self-proclaimed water lover. Before cancer I never went to work without a water bottle. I chugged water before my morning coffee just to get the day's water allotment started. I could never imagine someone saying those four words.

That Friday I found myself lying in bed just willing the nausea to release its grip, distracting myself with daydreams of being cancer-free and all the exciting places I'd visit.

Oh, how the breeze would feel nice on my barely bald head, bare feet on the sand, taking that first sip of morning coffee as the sun rose across the ocean.

That was a prettier picture than imagining the Carbo, like gasoline molasses, swirling around inside me, stubbornly stuck to my sluggish bowels.

By Friday evening I couldn't keep anything down. I knew I was severely dehydrated and had to go to the ER for fluids.

I was so nauseas, I curled up in a ball waiting for the nurse to start my IV, trying to magically transport myself back to that beach. But there was no sand between my toes, no sun caressing my skin. The hospital bed was cold and unyielding. I wrapped the warm blanket around my shoulders.

The saline drip began and I smiled gratefully at the nurse.

"Thank you," I whispered. "Water makes me gag."

Divine Intervention

Two particular negative aspects of going through chemo during a pandemic was having low white blood cell counts and people keeping their distance.

I spent a lot of days fearing an infection that my body couldn't fight off. I had headed in for chemo one morning, only to find out that I wasn't *allowed* to get the infusion. My neutrophil count was terrifyingly low, too low apparently for the body to handle chemo.

What a shock! Who knew in just a short period of time, I'd be devastated to find out I couldn't get chemotherapy? I'd come to welcome it. I didn't want to prolong this marathon by even one extra week.

To make matters worse, this was a period of time when we were constantly hearing statistics about how many people had died from COVID.

I headed home to quarantine even more strictly than usual.

The women who were diagnosed with breast cancer before me were surrounded by loved ones. I imagined their best friends dropping by to show love in person. A home-cooked meal here, a rom-com in bed there. I imagined my children's friends' mothers scooping them up for distracting playdates, so they weren't constantly exposed to mom being ill on sick days. And lastly, I imagined walking into a breast cancer support group where the chairs were filled with bald heads, and we all laughed at how bad the coffee tasted with our metallic mouths.

I wanted it all. I had none of it.

Thankfully I had "met" women in the triple-negative support group on Facebook, and we were texting daily.

Lexi comforted me and encouraged me to enjoy the one-week break from chemo.   She and I sent each other our charts to compare notes.   Her counts were strong. Neither of us had ever heard of having to skip because of neutrophils or even had heard that word before!   We both asked around and it turns out it's not uncommon and some people have to skip a few infusions.

Back in The Chair for my next round of treatment, I waited nervously for my blood count report to come back.

I was sitting across from an older woman getting chemo who was sitting next to what looked to be her daughter. Her daughter had very short hair.

The younger woman turned to me and said, "Excuse me, but are you Cara?"

I learned a long time ago never to assume someone was recognizing me from the news. Because it never failed if I said, "I am a reporter for Channel 11 News…"

They'd say, "No, no that is not it."

"No, I don't watch the news."

"No, I've never seen you on TV."

It was always embarrassing when that happened.

Once in line for a bagel, a lady said, "Excuse me, are you Cara Sapida?" I said yes. She continued, "I love you on WDVE!"   WDVE is a morning radio show where I occasionally fill in reading the news of the day. She told me she's never caught me on the news but looked up my photo on the WDVE website. So again, I never assume.

Back in the chemo room, the short-haired woman introduced herself as Emily and said she recognized me from a Pittsburgh moms Facebook group. She was there to support her mother who was going through cancer treatment. She said the year before she had finished chemo herself for triple-negative breast cancer. I was so taken aback by this. This beautiful, healthy human sitting in front of me had recently beaten my cancer. I did the math real fast and estimated there were at least forty chairs in my cancer center, with approximately two to three women who sit in The Chair each day, and she was sitting across from me.

I learned Emily had almost my exact diagnosis and like me was also BRCA1 positive. And now she was on the other side of her treatment, back to her life as a mom of two little boys. She told me she was making plans to take them to the zoo. The zoo! I could only dream of the day.

My medical team highly encouraged walking for exercise. It hadn't been working out great for me. My days consisted mostly of remaining in bed, crawling out of bed, getting back into bed, trying to play with the kids before I napped in bed and going to the cancer center for treatment. This lovely pixie-sporting mother was *taking her kids to the zoo.*

A friend of mine once told me there is no such thing as coincidences, just "God winks". I googled it. A *God wink* is an event or personal experience, often identified as coincidence, so astonishing that it is seen as a sign of divine intervention.

In this moment, I discovered why I didn't need to research my disease online, or seek out facts, figures, and statistics. All I needed to see was right in front of me.

Emily and I swapped phone numbers. I told her I had recently deleted Facebook and she said she didn't have an Instagram, so we formed our friendship the old-school way.

My nurse came back with the good news that my counts were just barely high enough to get the infusion. I'll take it!

Emily and her mom said goodbye, and we planned to keep in touch. I made a friend while almost exclusively quarantined during a pandemic.

Cheers to divine intervention, I thought. And then the Benadryl knocked me out.

The Storm

I think we've established that chemo is no walk in the park. But around this halfway mark I found myself fearlessly, boldly walking into my cancer center. There was a hitch in my giddy-up that even I couldn't deny.

Each treatment felt like a mile marker on that involuntary marathon. The finish line wasn't in sight, but I felt it in the distance for the first time. The gauntlet had just a few remaining obstacles.

I was capitalizing on my strong days and really leaning into feeling well. I could envision what it would be like to feel well all week, week after week, and how that could be cumulative, too.

I felt so positive after a few days of feeling well, that I believed maybe the sick days wouldn't hit me this week. When the nausea did hit, it surprised me a bit. If I could just drive home this marathon analogy, it's like feeling the breeze in your hair as you run downhill, feeling like you've really hit your stride with a sustainable pace, when bam! You get sideswiped by a runaway dump truck.

My Carbo chemo weeks, specifically, just kept knocking me down.

The night before my final Carbo I couldn't sleep, just dreading what was coming my way. Carbo had already sent me to the ER twice for fluids. I finally gave up on sleep and trudged downstairs to make coffee at 4:30 a.m. I knew it would be the last coffee I had for at least a week. Chemo metal mouth and coffee did not mix. Try swirling a few tablespoons of vinegar in your morning cup, and you'll see what I mean.

I sat down on the kitchen floor to wait for the pot to brew, and where lately I'd done a lot of reflecting. I found myself humming that popular nursery song: "Can't go under it, can't go around it..." You know the song. I had to go through it.

I had the will to beat this cancer, but damn if I didn't just want to take a short cut—it's human nature. I saw myself in the middle of that marathon, barefoot with a broken 80's Walkman, still trying to figure out who signed me up for this shit. I could almost see a hidden alleyway just begging me to sneak through.

Quick, just get to the finish line and put it all behind you!

But there was something I desired even more, and that was killing every cancer cell in my body.

I found myself back in The Chair, this time wearing a personalized mask, sent to me that week by my friends Moe and Nika. When I had opened up the care package, I got emotional because written on the mask was a line from my new favorite quote.

The quote was written in that comment on my Facebook post revealing my diagnosis:

> "Fate whispered to the warrior, 'You cannot withstand the storm.' And the warrior whispered back, 'I am the storm.'"

It is hard to feel like a warrior, no matter how many people will say it, when you mostly feel sick. How many warriors do you know who cannot walk around the block without getting winded? Metaphorically, I felt like a fighter if only because chemo kept knocking me down and I kept getting back up.

And this single quote helped channel my inner warrior that day because suddenly I felt ready for the poison, the nausea, the fighting through and getting back up again.

The mask said: *I Am The Storm*.

It's okay if you're not skipping and whistling into chemo. It's okay to crawl. It's enough just to show up. Chemo is cumulative, as we've established, and it is a dirty rotten conniving sneak. And even worse, a thief. It steals hair and energy and will try to break you. It will try to keep you down.

Just remember, there is a tribe of women in your corner screaming for you to get back up again.

We know it all too well, from our days in the storm.

Breast Cancer Awareness Month

T he halfway point for my chemotherapy treatment landed smack in the middle of October.

I had all but blinked and I was past the Dark Days, having completed the first round of twelve treatments.

I altered my perspective after my breakdown: I started to welcome those treatments. I tried to walk into the cancer center with a determination on my face, filled with belief and conviction that chemo was doing its job. Each treatment was one step closer to the end of this dark tunnel. I was carefully checking off the weekly milestones when suddenly I reached the halfway point.

There's a theme here that maybe I'm not driving home hard enough about why I decided to write this book. But if I could just go back in time, I'd ask a little more boldly for more warnings. More warnings about all aspects of this so-called journey. But really, why didn't anyone warn me about October?! I discovered that the entire month of October was a trigger.

I woke on October first and my social media feeds suddenly reflected my life: wall-to-wall breast cancer! Except where my life was heavy with pain, anguish, bitterness, nausea, and a tiny bit of humor on my good days, my timeline was PINK.

Among the ribbons I stumbled on a quote that said, "Breast cancer is

more than pink ribbons."

Now that stopped my scrolling.

I looked around my bedroom at the always full water bottle because water still made me gag. I spotted my new wig on the Styrofoam head collecting dust because wearing it felt disingenuous during this period of my life. I looked at a dozen pill bottles carefully lined on my nightstand and dreamed of the day I could take my forearm and swipe them all into the garbage. I glanced at the new jewelry holder, purchased to house all the gifts sent to me from thoughtful friends, engraved with everything from "warrior" to "fuck cancer."

I looked at the mirror that still hung on my wall, but I now walked past with purpose—that purpose being avoidance.

Not a pink ribbon in sight.

Breast cancer is ugly.

It's not being able to look yourself in the mirror most days.

It's the inability to avoid the mirror after a shower, so you hang your head instead.

It's forgetting you don't have hair at least once a day and finding a bald head instead.

It's subconsciously touching the port that will forever scar your chest.

It scars across your chest and soul, ugly.

It's not being able to find the right words, on the first day of October, because more than halfway through this experience it's still so raw. And so ugly.

I continued to scroll with growing outrage.

I stopped on a fellow breast cancer fighter's post about this awareness month. She wrote, "My words are not coming, so I'm just sitting in my feelings."

I think there is a great deal of awareness for breast cancer these days, and I'm grateful for it. I'm grateful for the research that's being done to find a cure. As I type this, there is a human trial beginning for a triple-negative *vaccine*, and that kind of news fills me with hope.

And I encourage anyone interested in celebrating Breast Cancer Awareness Month to make a donation, large or small, to a local breast cancer nonprofit—a group working to support women at all stages of their diagnosis every day. Please consider doing this. Or make a donation to an organization working on medical research to improve breast cancer treatment and advancements each year.

I am thankful for every "pink campaign" that gets women to do self-breast exams or schedule mammograms.

But commercialization of this ugly, life-changing disease with phrases like "my boobs tried to kill me" is hard to read while you're still in the fight.

According to the CDC and the American Cancer Society, about one in eight women will be diagnosed with breast cancer. One in eight! If you catch it early enough, there's a chance you won't have to experience the ugliest of the ugly. Spreading awareness, in hopes of guiding women toward early detection and saving lives, is critical.

And sadly, due to the COVID-19 pandemic, many mammograms were postponed.

If giving October a label helps get women to schedule those appointments, then I support it. But I'm sitting in my feelings until I figure out a way to do it better. I have some ideas that I'm still working out. But plenty of women have spoken out beautifully about this. Plenty of organizations are speaking out against 'pinkwashing', and against large companies greedily profiting off October pink labels.

You don't need to glamorize such an ugly disease to spread awareness. We can do better.

Because for the women in the thick of it, breast cancer is not pink ribbons.

THE METAMORPHOSIS

My girlfriend Kate comforted me when I was in the Dark Days, depressed over both the breast cancer diagnosis and the divorce. She told me I was going to come through the other side as a new, stronger woman. A full metamorphosis, she said.

I planned to meet Kate for lunch after my big ultrasound that determined the size of my tumor after twelve chemo treatments. It was my first ultrasound since the one revealing I had breast cancer. I knew my tumor was initially 1.8cm, and rapidly grew to 3cm in the few weeks before chemo started. They don't call triple-negative the fastest growing for nothing. That little bastard *grew*.

Thanks to Covid I hadn't met anyone for lunch, or any meal in public, for months. But during my break from chemo and knowing I may get devastating results from the ultrasound, I agreed to meet her.

I got naked from the waist up and waited for my scan. Ask any breast cancer fighter, and we can take out our boobs and assume the position in ten seconds flat. Breasts are no longer a body part I think of as sexy. They betrayed me and would soon be removed, and no less than twenty medical professionals have felt, studied, and tested them.

A young woman came in and said she was studying to be an ultrasound technologist and she would be doing my scan first, then the actual tech, and then the radiologist. (The last time a medical student practiced on me I did pass out, but that's another story, and still I welcome helping anyone studying in this field.)

She placed my arm above my head and told me the gel would be cold. The gel at my initial ultrasound that found the cancer was warm. It's a minor difference but comfort level variation is something I often note at hospitals now.

She spent some time moving her wand-looking probe all around my breast and making small talk. I can't remember one subject we discussed during those agonizingly long minutes because my stomach was wrecked. I started off brave, whipping my shirt and bra off like some fearless breast cancer warrior, but fear began to paralyze my limbs. I will never have a stress-free ultrasound again in my life.

A quick knock on the door and the tech came in. She explained the situation to me again, how she was helping train this student and just going to talk her through the process. I turned my head away in fear of what teaching out loud would reveal.

The tech told the student not to be embarrassed if she was struggling to locate the tumor. She suggested the student try to look for the tumor marker, or clip, that was inserted by the radiologist during a biopsy to mark the spot. (Clips look like tiny charms. For example, a heart and a ribbon are just a couple tumor clip names I've heard mentioned along the way.)

Or, the tech said, just ask the patient. She assured her that every single woman she's ever done an ultrasound on could show you exactly where her tumor was located. I know this to be true because most women feel their tumor for changes every day. I wasn't one of those women, and I hadn't touched my tumor in nearly three months.

I directed her to my spot immediately.

The nurse took over the probe and moved it around the breast and said, "You couldn't find it because there is nothing left to measure."

My head whipped around.

She smiled at me and said, "This is amazing. Your chemo is working. Your body is doing the work too. There is no tumor left that we can see."

A tear I didn't even feel sneaking up on me slid down my cheek.

"There is nothing left?" I asked.

"Nothing the naked eye can see on an ultrasound. This doesn't mean there aren't residual cancer cells there, but we can't see anything."

I knew if there were still cancer cells there, I had four more intensive, brutal rounds of chemotherapy left that I prayed would annihilate them.

The student looked at the screen closer and asked, "Is that the marker? I think I see a coil."

"Yes, all that's left is that marker. But it's not a coil," the nurse replied. "It's a butterfly."

My friend, Kate, cried at lunch when I told her this update. Every test before now had knocked me down, one blow after another. Together we cried tears of joy and hope. And that's when Kate said:

"A butterfly clip? How symbolic. I told you this was going to be your metamorphosis."

THE MONSTER

Armed with fresh knowledge that my treatments were working, a flicker of hope was lit and it couldn't have come at a better time. Suddenly my face reflected what I was feeling inside most days: sick as hell.

Shouting from the rooftops that you're doing well and putting up a brave fight is easier to do when you don't look ill. I'd hardly left the house over the last month, just to and from the chemo chair. But the few places I went, I proactively smiled at folks, hoping to ward off any pity looks. *Really doing great*, my smiling face tried to say.

That week, I got a phone call from Jen, the founder of the Young Women's Breast Cancer Awareness Foundation, asking me if I'd like to participate in a professional photoshoot to help raise breast cancer awareness.

Did I?

I had about seven eyelashes left on one eye and four on the other. My lids were rimmed with irritation. I was painfully, frighteningly pale. And while I was completely bald, some random sparse hairs sprouted and could be seen blowing in the wind if the light was right.

I said yes. Finding purpose through the pain felt like an attainable goal and I wanted to do my part to raise awareness.

The day of the photoshoot I sat down to put on makeup for the first time in months. I colored in my brow area, which had also dwindled down to nearly nothing, and dug up the brightest lipstick in my drawer. I'd ordered magnetic eyelashes just for this occasion, drawing a thick line with the magnetic eyeliner and popping them on. *Fun! That was easy*, I thought.

I stared in the mirror for a long time, thinking something didn't look quite right. It must be my pale, hairless face full of bold makeup that looked weird to me. At the time, I didn't realize my fake eyelashes were actually on the wrong *sides*. The longer ends were facing inward, like they were attacking my nose. A novice at wearing lashes, I didn't even know they weren't interchangeable!

I descended the steps like it was prom, ready for my kids to be blown away, after seeing me look so sick every day. Greyson gasped. "You look like a monster!"

"What?!"

My son *never* talked to me like this. His words stung.

"What is on your eyes!? Take them off! PLEASE! You look like a monster!"

I said, "Greyson, that hurts my feelings. Why would you say that to Mommy?"

And he whispered with typical gut-wrenching sincerity, "Have you looked in a mirror?"

The boy who has loved and complimented me on my Darkest Days, the boy who told me right after I shaved my head that I still look beautiful—did not love my bold magnetic lashes on the wrong eyes. I explained to him that the eyelashes were fake and made me feel pretty. And if you don't have anything nice to say, don't say anything at all. *Thanks, Grandma, for that life lesson I'm passing on to my kids today.* And out the door we went.

Jen, the photographer, my kids, my mom, and I met up for the big shoot. It takes a village! I had my entourage as we walked to the alleyway. I felt very exposed on a public sidewalk, in my bright floral dress and big bald head.

In the alley, she snapped a few solo photos of me and then told the kids to jump in. As always, Greyson's arms flew around my neck and Lilah jumped into my arms. I immediately felt grateful to have these photos and capture the purest love I'll ever know.

After the photo shoot we started walking back to the car when the photographer said I should take one more photo, on these beautiful old stone stairs. I climbed a few stairs and sat down, crossed my legs and smiled—when a woman driving past leaned out of her car window and yelled something we couldn't hear. She slowed her car and shouted it again.

The photographer smiled and said, "She said you're stunning."

My jaw dropped as my brain tried to compute. I felt both disbelief and gratitude for this compliment from a passing stranger. I imagine it's instinctual for people to look away from our bald heads. I was so taken aback by her kind words.

That night, with the makeup washed off, I looked in the bathroom mirror and thought, *This is when I look like a monster.*

I didn't mean to think it, but I just did. Like a clown washing off a face full of paint, only to discover a sad face underneath. I threw the fake lashes in the trash. But my son, in all his innocence, showed me that is not how he sees me at all. He didn't need me to paint my face.

So I dragged my head back up to the mirror, and tried this out on my tongue instead: "You're stunning."

And then I cried. I hope wherever you are standing in your fight against breast cancer you can take to heart this quote from Thoreau, "It's not what you look at that matters, it's what you see."

And while I avoided mirrors a lot during treatment, I stopped putting myself down. I just saw a mother beating the real monster— breast cancer.

Photos by: Requiem Images

CHEMO IS CUMULATIVE

In the beginning of my Dark Days, a few of my new breast cancer survivor friends told me that "chemo is cumulative."

They warned me that the side effects catch up with you and assured me this was normal, saying just don't be caught off guard or upset when it happens.

I remember wishing they would stop saying that. That kind of talk caused me great frustration, as I felt like I was really staying on top of the beast and showing it who's boss.

Cumulative chemo effects were their stories. *Just because the side effects cumulatively progressed for other women, doesn't mean that had to be the case for me*, I remember thinking.

I was drinking thirty-six ounces of raw green juice a day. I told myself, *The tribe has voted. I'm going to slay this cancer like the chemo warrior I was elected to be. Side effects will not slow me down.*

As a mom, one of the most important qualities I'm working to teach my children is to be honest, which includes admitting when you're wrong.

This shit is cumulative, and there is no getting around it.

It really caught up to me right as I was starting "The Red Devil."

One of the most frequent questions I'm asked is about my experience with the chemotherapy drug Adriamycin and Cytoxan, also known as A/C, also nicknamed The Red Devil.

The Red Devil is a popular topic in group chats and cancer meetings. And while everyone's experience is different, collectively most of us hate it.

Adriamycin and Cytoxan is a bright red drug that has to be slowly pushed into your body via a giant syringe, instead of hung in a bag and entered in a drip like most chemotherapy drugs. Your oncology nurse has to suit up in full protective gear—picture a hazmat situation here—to administer it. It is so potent, so *poisonous*, that nurses actually need to protect their body from it. And it is injected right into our blood stream.

A lot of women with my diagnosis get A/C first, but I was on an immunotherapy trial, and we had a different order. I did Taxol for the first twelve weeks, just dreading it and knowing it was coming. When it was my time to start on the Red Devil, my body was already pretty beat up from the previous twelve chemotherapy treatments.

On the days following the A/C treatment, I discovered I couldn't take care of my children or myself. My mother had uprooted her whole life and lived with us through it all. Before A/C, she helped take care of the kids, while dispensing medicine around the clock, cooking all our meals and making fresh juices. But I was out of bed, capable and parenting.

During A/C, every week following treatment I was mostly stuck in bed. My mom and the kids colored me pictures and the kids would decorate the bed, the walls, the nightstand, and the window. Almost a year out from treatment, one of those drawings was still in my bedroom window.

I felt a bone-deep exhaustion. I'd come home from my cancer center, give hugs and kisses on the move, then go straight up the stairs and into my bed.

My friend from high school, Jen, told me after her first A/C treatment she was able to drive all the way home *by herself*, got out of her car, even opened her front door before unexpectedly getting slammed down. She crawled on her hands and knees the rest of the way to bed, where she slept for two days.

"Is it worse than Carbo? Is it more nausea or exhaustion? Is it more bone pain or headache? Do you sleep for one whole day or one whole week? Do you get one week off between A/C infusions, or two, or three?" Those are a few of the questions women ask after learning they'll be getting this infusion.

If you do read about it, and even if I warn you today and your nurse warns you in the moment, you'll still be startled when you go pee after your infusion and your urine is red.

For the first time in my treatment, instead of repeating my Glennon Doyle mantra—*you can do hard things*—I found myself face first in a pillow saying, *You cannot do hard things. You cannot do this.*

From the bed to the toilet I went for four days. I slept all day, waking to pee and catch waves of nausea so intense I believed my body just went back to sleep for me.

My Red Devil infusions were every other week. So, I'd find myself starting to feel better by the end of the first week. And something wonderful happened, and I mean *wonderful*. I'd get a whole week feeling decent. And you know what? Feeling decent is also cumulative. By the end of week two, I felt damn near strong again. I could do all the motherly things and give my children a sense of normalcy. I finally could go for those walks my medical team recommended.

And while each A/C was worse than the one before, I knew it came with that free week off. And sometimes you just have to compartmentalize the bad weeks and focus on the good. Every time you get a good week following your bad one, you're one step closer to the finish line.

I hope you have a support system for your hard days. I think back on that time, and I'm grateful for my mom who put her life on hold while I was fighting for mine.

Just Keep Serving the Peanuts

There isn't enough therapy, and there aren't enough words of wisdom for anyone diagnosed with cancer with young children. Those cumulative chemo effects weren't just hard on my body, but my heart. The sickness and nausea really just meant less energy for my kids.

It was around this time that I opened up Facebook and read a post about parenting that greatly helped.

My friend Randy, an ESPN sports anchor, lost his mother not long after he had become a father. Randy is a wonderful writer who memorialized his mother, a former flight attendant, posting about her spirit and warmth on holidays and birthdays. His writing was poetic. It always made this woman larger than life to me. I never met her, but I would hang on his every word.

"Mom knew the importance of 'serving the peanuts' with kids. No matter how bad the turbulence gets: they'll look to you to see if you're calm and smiling, so keep serving the peanuts and keep things positive and as normal as possible."

There was so much out of my control, but this single phrase felt doable.

I tried to stick to our routines, to give some semblance of normalcy through it all. Our favorite nightly routine was reading books. I read to Greyson and Lilah almost every night that I wasn't sick or asleep before their bedtime. I didn't always have enough energy to read to both children separately, so I plopped a bean bag chair in the hall between their two bedrooms. I refused to give up this cherished time together, that I'd come to love as a mother, so I modified it. They'd run into the hall to look at the pictures and jump back onto their beds. It became a fun game.

I didn't tell them just reading aloud could wipe me out because I knew as soon as they were tucked in, I could go straight to sleep myself.

Our morning routine had to be modified as well. Before cancer, the kids would wake me up and we'd go straight downstairs and dive right into the day. Now they'd just carefully crawl into bed with me. The country was shut down, schools were closed, and no one was visiting because of COVID scares. We had nowhere to be but there. And so, we snuggled. Even while my heart ached for what I'd lost, I was grateful for what I'd gained: uninterrupted time with my favorite small humans.

How lucky was I?

We found ourselves managing a new normal.

Without my old energy, I gave myself permission to just rest, knowing I was only a day or two away from being more present. I gave myself permission to eat meals with my kids in my bed. I forced myself to do nothing but try and drink the water that makes you gag.

It's okay if you're just going through the motions without feeling much of anything because the body and brain can feel pretty numb sometimes, a defense mechanism to protect you and keep you out of the fetal position.

But looking back, I think my kids were just happy to have Mommy home. How lucky were we?

You just have to keep serving the peanuts.

TAKE THE PHOTOS

I think you should take the photos.

From the day of my diagnosis, I've been just as eager as the cancer fighters before me, and those who came after, to put it all behind me.

With all my might, and with all my determination, I want to erase this painful time from my past and wish it never changed my life course.

We can't. We can never.

But someday you'll look back and think how it flew by, and how it changed you and your outlook, and just maybe you'll wish you captured some raw moments.

Sentimental, beautiful photos of my children and me arrived in the mail in the middle of my chemo. In the whirlwind since finding my lump, life had changed so drastically, I'd forgotten I'd taken them.

Just days before I was set to start chemo, I had reached out to a family friend, David Burke, who is a professional photographer, and asked if he had any free time on such short notice.

At that point, I had no idea what would lie ahead of me.

But I knew I wanted my children to have photos of their Mommy before I lost my hair, before the unknown began.

He said he'd be over the next day.

We moved my patio couch into the middle of the yard, plopped down and smiled. Within minutes, my kids were off their butts, as most kids do when you're trying to take a nice picture. But they weren't running around the yard, they were crawling on top of me. My son wrapped his arms around my neck. My daughter lay her head on my lap. David directed none of it. These babies of mine were captured showing me their love, similar to how we cuddle on the living room couch each morning.

Photo by: David Burke

When the photos arrived a couple weeks later, I was already in treatment. I was a remnant of that woman in the pictures. My newly bald head was mostly smooth, kind of patchy, quite scary. Chemo or immunotherapy acne had taken over my face. I was getting paler by the week. There was already a new normal for our family as well, as our world was flipped upside down so suddenly. The photos were this painfully beautiful reminder of what just was, and hopefully what would be again someday.

I treasured them immediately. I treasured Greyson's huge smiles and Lilah's serious "resting toddler face." I loved seeing their little arms around my body. It would be these tiny arms that managed to lift me up most days.

At first, I clutched the photos to my chest and made plans to hang them on my mantle, the walls, maybe create an old-school coffee table album, but ended up putting them away. They went into hiding.

But my kids didn't seem to notice *at all*. To them, I was just mom without all that hair. I did not care if my hair grew back blond or brown, gray or purple, curly or straight. In fact, I had heard there was a strong chance it was coming back gray—fine by me, that felt stylish. I did not care. I just wanted the opportunity to have hair again because it meant this treatment would be over.

A woman in my triple-negative Facebook support group said her hair started coming in light gray before it turned brown, and she decided not to cut it. She was at the salon when another woman asked if she could get the same "white tips" done to her hair. The stylist said, "You do not want to go through what this woman did to get that hair."

Documenting my cancer-fight on paper, from day one, was important to me. It was harder to share photos of my big, bald head.

Before this experience I'd only had family photos taken once. I'd never been the mom to send holiday photos and the only ones I had taken growing up were from Glamour Shots in the mall.

But in November, a local Pittsburgh photographer, Melissa Lucci, offered to take holiday photos for me and the kids. She said someone close to her had been affected by breast cancer and she would like to take our photos for free.

It had been a month since the professional photos were taken with the kids for the breast cancer awareness shoot. And thanks to cumulative chemo, by this point I looked quite sick. Did I want more photos taken?

My lashes that had held on for dear life dwindled to a select few. With astonishingly beautiful timing, my brows all fell out the day before. I was sick, pale and hairless.

I said yes.

That morning, I dressed little Lilah in a black and white outfit and pink boots, Greyson in a grey sweater and jeans, and put on a new white sweater for myself with gold ribbons laced through it. There would be no fake lashes or clown face this time. I drew on some brows, slapped on some lip-gloss and headed out the door.

The studio was ultra-modern and industrial and pretty cool for my kids who had been stuck at home for months.

Greyson shouted, "Is this where the Kidz Bop Kids dance!?"

They turned on the charm, smiling and exuding pure joy. But I was nervous. I had wanted my kids to have those summertime couch photos, when their mom was a picture of health. What did the lens see now? Did it pity me? Did it see the pain in my eyes and fear these could be my last photos?

Lilah crawled into my lap, but instead of smiling for the camera she climbed up higher. With delicate tiny hands she cupped my face and gave me a kiss. She put her little fists under her chin, giving her best resting toddler face again. When it was Greyson's turn, he immediately did his signature move, wrapping his arms around my neck. I held his toddler hands, cherishing how they felt in my own, just like that day on the back stoop when I'd told him my silly hair would soon fall out.

Days later the photos arrived, with this note from Melissa in the email:

"I cannot imagine how you felt when we took these photos and how you're feeling right now. I can only guess, because I've held the hands of my sister, mother, grandma and

mother-in-law on their unique cancer journeys," Melissa wrote.

"Letting your kids crawl all over you, in a studio, in 2020, in front of a person you met just two minutes before... that's not easy. Nothing about what you're going through right now is easy... but mama, your courage and beauty are making it look that way. You're strong for those around you in true mama fashion.

I want no 'credit' if you decide to share these images, you certainly don't have to... it's an intimate time.

You might not feel it, but this phase looks beautiful on you and all your kids see is their mama showing up to love them through it. I promise that.

Keep fighting, feel it all, and look back on these when the hair starts to grow back. Always remember what a badass you are."

I wiped my wet cheeks on my face and opened the photos. They were unexpectedly beautiful, capturing a mother's love during the most painful days of my life. I thought to myself, *is this what resilience looks like?*

Breast cancer is not pink ribbons. Take your photos and share them. Don't put them in hiding. May the world not look away from our bald heads as we hold our babies.

Photos by: Melissa Lucci

#fcancer #fightlikeamother

MENTAL FORTITUDE

Yoga was a big part of my life before I had kids. The hotter, the better. I used to sweat buckets in hot yoga four nights a week, stretching my arms into warrior poses, inverting my body in headstands, challenging myself to land the crow, which is balancing your entire body on the backs on your forearms.

I told you how the instructors would tell us to look forward without focusing your eyes. They coached us to breathe. Deep breaths, in through the nose, out through the mouth.

A lot of yoga instructors say this part very slowly, "In-nnn throughhhh the nooooooooooose, and out through-hhhh the mouth."

In hot yoga, I felt the toxins leaving my body, carried away with the sweat. I noticed the calming effect on my brain, constantly overworked and full of anxiety and stress, from reporting on tragedy after tragedy.

Yoga was healing for me.

But it wasn't easy. It took *years* to build that mental fortitude to exercise in 100-degree Fahrenheit. When I first started, I had strong urges to laugh. Instead of focusing my eyes, they were straight up wonky, sneaking glances in every direction at the yogis who were in the zone while I was stuck in my head. When we'd invert, I'd stare at their butts and wonder if a fart was going to sneak out during this silent exercise. *Unfocus your eyes! Fix your thoughts and breathe, Cara!*

I put in the work. Eventually, yoga transformed my body and mind. Finally I could mentally check out and spend seventy glorious minutes without a thought in my head. I practiced throughout my entire first pregnancy, modifying the poses for safety and to get around my growing belly. But after the baby was born I suddenly didn't have the time or energy for it.

During the Dark Days, I found myself crawling out of the fetal position and into child's pose. If I was going to be on the ground, by God, I was going to try and calm myself. I didn't have the studio heat because the country was shut down. I started doing yoga from memory in my living room.

Two of the last photos I have with hair, taken before I handed my Aunt Darcie the pair of kitchen scissors, are doing half-moon poses in my kitchen. One arm on the ground, the other straight in the air. One leg on the ground, the other stretched back at a right angle. Half-moon is a fan favorite because it feels incredible. I challenged myself to lift my hand off the ground, a more difficult pose, like I'd easily do in the good old days. I fell over, but laughed at least.

I texted photos of myself in half-moon to my former yoga instructor, Mandy, who is also a stage II triple-negative breast cancer survivor. She is one of the first people I reached out to after my diagnosis. I asked her which photo had the best form.

Leave it to me to beat myself up over *form* at a time like this.

In the photos I saw arms that were not in a perfectly straight line, legs that looked short and stumpy, stomach notably wobbly and curly hair with inches of dark quarantine roots.

Three months later, from The Chair, I reviewed those photos. As chemo dripped into my bloodstream, I noticed how drastically my perspective had already changed— on almost everything in my life.

My form didn't look as bad as I remembered, or even bad at all for someone who hadn't taken a yoga class in years. I couldn't believe those negative thoughts were shuffling around in my head just a couple months prior, as I preached about putting positive energy into the world.

What I wouldn't give to have those curls back, roots and all! I thought about how many mornings I wasted time straightening that hair. Thousands of hours, at least.

I took for granted a body that gave birth to two babies and still executed kitchen floor yoga with strength and determination. I had made it a priority to feed my body well, but healthy food wasn't the only fuel I needed. I needed a mental reset.

I've met many survivors who say cancer didn't just turn their world upside down, but it also changed their perspective for the better. They came through it with a new appreciation for each day. They actually stopped sweating the small stuff.

Each hellish week that I suffered through physically was followed up by a week of building back strength and mental fortitude to do it again. Unlike yoga, I didn't have years to work on this, I had to catapult myself here mentally in a short amount of time. I wasn't just enduring the prison sentence that was my life on lockdown during chemo, or tolerating it, I was gaining tools to apply to the rest of my life. The overcoming adversity tool isn't something you're born with, or would eagerly sign up for, but it was tossed into my lap like a gift. I promised myself I was coming through this experience *stronger*. I vowed to be unwavering with my dedication to mental and physical health after cancer. I envisioned a life of peace and I was reaching for it.

My last chemo treatment was right around the corner. The enemy I'd pictured pulling a sneak attack on me was losing. My healthy-cell cancer fighters were kicking in the swinging doors like an old Western movie and smoking those cancer cells one by one. They were doing the physical work; the least I could do was the mental olympics.

The unexpected gift of mental fortitude feels like a secret in the breast cancer sisterhood community.

Let's vow to one another to accept positive energy only, including from our brains to ourselves.

Yoga instructor Mandy got the photos and texted me back that day, when I asked which photo had better form.

She replied: "Well first I can tell you're holding your breath, so breathe."

In through the nose, out through the mouth. We've got this.

Heaven's Church

Note: I mentioned how I've learned that many women go through breast cancer while going through another hardship. I met a woman who was going through a tragedy too big and too painful to call a hardship. She was experiencing what's arguably the worst a parent can endure. She's asked me when my book is going to be published and she isn't afraid to share her story, but if it's too much, skip on. And if you can, don't look away.

With just a few weeks left until I finished chemo, I decided I could open Facebook and browse for the first time in months. I wanted to take some time and thank everyone for their outpouring of love and support.

I still wasn't ready to tackle the messages, the stories of loss, or the people who were adamantly insisting on what treatments I should and shouldn't undergo.

After my diagnosis, when I was still posting my updates regularly on social media, I had such a hard time reading some of the comments. I had felt pressure to reply to everyone, but some commenters had stories that were too difficult for me to digest.

Sadly, so many people have been affected by this awful disease, and I couldn't handle hearing every story when I was still trying to navigate and understand my diagnosis.

That morning, I started the coffee maker and opened Facebook.

The very first post that popped up was from DeAnna, a local mother I had interviewed in January of 2019, in one of the most heartbreaking tragedies I'd ever, ever covered.

On many occasions the stories I covered were so gut-wrenching, my photographer and I would often drive back to the TV station in silence, just staring out the window. But I always managed to keep my composure until the cameras stopped rolling—except on this day.

This story was a fatal house fire that killed two children. A young brother and sister found in their bedroom by first responders, arms wrapped around one another. Seven-year-old Ryleigh was undoubtedly protecting her younger brother, five-year-old Gunner, in their last minutes. I had just become a mother of two myself, and my ache for DeAnna, this mother who lost her children, was unbearable.

I met the local pastor outside their church, and she shared something that had happened with DeAnna's family during the previous week's church services. I couldn't stop thinking about it. She had told me Ryleigh stood up in church and made an announcement.

Soon it was 6 p.m., and my story was airing. I told the details of a fire breaking out in this family's home, of parents desperately trying to push through a wall of flames to reach their children.

I took a deep breath.

Barely able to get out the words, I choked a bit as I said what I'd learned, "This family's pastor told us that this young girl found courage to stand up in church last week and said, 'Please pray for my mom. She is fighting breast cancer.'"

That day I ended my story choking on my words as the tears escaped down my cheeks.

There was no way to know of my own breast cancer diagnosis just months away. There was no way to predict how my own children, also a girl and a boy, would spend their nights asking God to pray for Mommy.

But I imagined it and felt it deeply.

Opening Facebook that morning, I saw a post from DeAnna. She wanted to share some news that she just had her latest round of scans after being diagnosed with stage IV breast cancer and was holding the results. I hadn't even known her cancer progressed. In fact, I'd never seen a single post from DeAnna before this day. She wrote that her doctors couldn't explain it, but she had no evidence of disease anywhere in her body.

She wrote how her doctor said, "You're a walking miracle, mama. You're in remission!"

I sat on my kitchen floor clutching my bald head and letting out an ugly cry.

Eventually I picked my phone back up and opened her post again. DeAnna wrote, "It completely took my breath away! The only thing I could do in that moment was cry and stare at the ceiling because, as I said before, my heart lives not only in me but in my support system and most importantly in my angel babies."

I could smell the coffee now. It had finished brewing but I couldn't get to my feet. I just quietly wept on the kitchen floor for this strong mother.

Doctors may not be able to explain it, but this I know for sure: a seven-year-old angel stood up in heaven's church with a request.

And prayers were answered.

Don't you ever give up.

Oh, the Places You'll Go Fighting Cancer

When I had first started chemo, nighttime cuddles were both meaningful and hard on my heart. The ache of fear was a physical pain in my chest. I wanted all their nighttime snuggles and I was terrified of how many I would get.

My son had prayed.

"Dear God, please heal Mommy's boobies by morning. Thank you. Amen." That was his very first bedtime prayer after I explained to him that I breast cancer.

About halfway through my chemo treatment, one night he prayed, "Dear God, I have prayed for Mommy's boobies HUNDREDS OF TIMES ALREADY. Maybe sixty million times. Please make them all better."

Sixty million was his go-to favorite number since becoming obsessed with dinosaurs and when they roamed the planet.

One of the books we often read was a Dr. Seuss classic, *Oh, the Places You'll Go*. Every night, as I read this book, I was getting unexpectedly choked up. The book starts out strong, with bright, happy thoughts of going to great places where good things happen:

> *Wherever you fly, you'll be best of the best.*
> *Wherever you go, you will top all the rest.*

And then, bam! Seuss hits you with this:

> *Except when you don't.*
> *Because, sometimes, you won't.*
> *I'm sorry to say so*
> *But, sadly it's true*
> *that Bang-ups and Hang-ups can happen to you.*

What a life lesson from the good doctor. And while I'm glad my children have a book like this to prepare them for life's ups and downs, I was so deep in my downward spiral that the words gutted me. I'd say my final goodnights, extra hugs and kisses, and barely close the door before the tears came.

I'd cry while I brushed my teeth in the bathroom mirror and look away. I began brushing my teeth facing the shower or sitting on the bathroom floor. I washed my face and turned to dry it, avoiding the mirror altogether. I'd go to bed reciting these words against my will, *except when you don't because sometimes you won't.*

One of those nights I woke gasping around 3 a.m.— which wasn't uncommon. But on this night I started to write. I wrote the beginning of a poem that I ended up adding more verses to as each chemo passed. The final version is different from my middle-of-the-night original, mostly because the more treatment I survived, the more my perspective deepened.

But the two original stanzas that never changed were written at 3 a.m.:

> *Except when you don't*
> *because sometimes you won't*
> *sometimes you'll cry*
> *and ask yourself why*
> *I'm sorry to say*
> *but sadly it's true*
> *that bad days and bad weeks*
> *will happen to you*

It may sound simple, but this is the rawest truth about breast cancer if you have been recently diagnosed. The bad days are coming. And no matter how many friends, family members, or strangers call you a fighter, you will not always be fighting-ready. You will have days where you're ready to pull the covers over your head and hope to feel better in the morning. You might even have days where being called a fighter doesn't work for you. And that's fine too. Throw the label off and be whatever it is that you want. For me, I just wanted to be a mother.

Dear Breast Cancer Fighter
Dear breast cancer fighter
you're brave and you're strong
you're fierce and determined
in a race that is long
With grace goes the hair
that falls to your feet
a warrior now
prepare to defeat
You're never alone
a tribe by your side
millions who never
signed up for this ride
A glance in the mirror
familiar at best
with scars on your heart
your body
your chest
Inhale and exhale

kick down those doors
the cancer is weak
the warrior roars
Except when you don't
because sometimes you won't
sometimes you'll cry
and ask yourself why
I'm sorry to say
but sadly it's true
that bad days and bad weeks
will happen to you
And when you're alone
there will come a day
the sorrow and sadness
just won't go away
Both daydreams and nightmares
a frightening con
that may scare you so much
you won't want to go on
But on you will go
though the weather is foul
On you will go
while your cancer may prowl
On to the chair
and the poisonous drips
On with both courage
and prayers on your lips

On with the strength
only you can discover
through the eyes of your child
as you fight like a mother
Through the scans and the scares
the sympathy the stares
You are the storm
keep
climbing
the
stairs
Because the end is in sight
time to gather that might
throw off the label
you are more than this fight
And your day is coming
like the women before
fling your head back
rise up off the floor
With a face full of grace
and a head held up high
tears full of joy
take their turn to cry
Lift up that arm
and reach for the bell
the future is yours
say goodbye to your hell

THE LAST CHEMO

Two weeks before Christmas, I walked into the cancer center for my last chemotherapy treatment. The kids weren't allowed to join me-- due to a recent COVID mandate, that I had hoped would be lifted by now. On some of my darkest mornings, I had envisioned dropping to my knees to hug them in the hallway after this milestone. I pictured them excited to watch me ring the bell, marking the end of my treatment. I even pictured us laughing as I tried to pull the bell's rope with two kids in my arms.

My double mastectomy was scheduled. I knew after that surgery I wouldn't be able or allowed to lift anything for months. After all these grueling treatments, I was at my weakest and already couldn't carry my son. Breast cancer is a conniving thief that robbed me of this joy as it had everything else. Looking back, I probably could have squeezed in a few more lifts and hugs, but he's too big now.

My best friend from high school, Katie, travelled from Washington D.C. to drive me to the hospital and sit by my side for the last chemo. Old friends are such a gift, and I experienced a strong sense of gratitude as we pulled into the parking lot. It had been a lonely six months. But on this day, with Katie by my side, I did not feel alone.

I approached the hospital, head lowered, focusing on one foot in front of the other. That's what a marathon is after all, a whole lot of steps, one after another. Plenty of marathon runners talk about hitting a wall. I'm sure trainers tell them to dig deep and press on. Bystanders on the sidelines urging you forward. You can have all the support in the world, but it is lonely. No one can do it for you.

This final treatment had felt so far away. This moment had been just out of my reach, as I checked off treatment after treatment, week after week.

I suddenly heard cheering and my head shot up. On a cold December morning, standing outside the front doors of my hospital, were more friends. I saw balloons and big posters that said, "You are the storm!" They shouted, "We love you!"

I sobbed as I crossed the street. I sobbed as I thanked them. I sobbed as I headed in for one last round. And I did not feel alone.

My favorite nurse, Roseann, suited up in her hazmat outfit to give me one last Red Devil. Roseann felt like family to me. When I'd see signs outside the hospital that said, "Heroes Work Here", I'd think of Roseann. She conveyed warmth and sincerity while never sugarcoating the process.

This final Red Devil treatment finished entering my body. Roseann pulled the needle from my port. I felt overwhelmed with disbelief that it was over. She gave me a one-armed, masked hug and I didn't want her to let go. I said when the pandemic was over I was coming back for a full-body, huge hug.

One last trip to the restroom bracing for the bright red pee.

Another young woman fighting breast cancer, Gina, snuck down from the radiation floor and into the infusion room to give me cupcakes. It was such a thoughtful gesture. We made plans to meet up and go to brunch now that both of our chemo regimens were ending---and we had high hopes food would taste great again soon.

With my mom and Katie by my side we approached a circle of nurses who were waiting at the end of hall, next to the bell.

My mom said thank you to the nurses and Roseann replied, "From one mother to another, you're welcome."

These incredible nurses were clapping, like family and friends on the last leg of a marathon.

They were a constant source of support every step of the way.

Roseann told me to read the plaque under the bell, and I read aloud:

"Ring this bell, three times well, it's toll to clearly say, my treatment's done, this course is run, and I am on my way."

I reached for the rope and I rang it.

On the way home a short time later, I knew the final A/C nap and nausea were coming. I knew this final hard week would be the ugliest because chemo is cumulative. Call it adrenaline or relief it was the last one, but I felt extra energy as we drove down my street. That's when I heard more cheering.

In a kind, unexpected gesture that I greatly appreciated; my soon-to-be ex-husband had bought bells for the kids.

On a cold December afternoon, waiting in the driveway, my children cheered and rang their little bells. With them in my arms, I never felt alone. How lucky to have this waiting for me at the finish line.

THE DOUBLE MASTECTOMY

For a long time, I thought the end of treatment meant the beginning of feeling stronger every day. It wasn't a linear progression, though.

Emotionally, I wasn't even in recovery yet. Finishing treatment was an incredible accomplishment and an end to the grueling chemo marathon. But it was also the beginning of fear and guilt. It's a level of anxiety I was completely ill prepared to navigate.

I'd known since my second meeting with my surgeon that I'd have a double mastectomy after treatment. I had the BRCA1 genetic mutation, and that put me at high risk for breast cancer. A lumpectomy was never part of my plan.

Four weeks after my last chemo, I was wheeled into an operating room for this major surgery, scheduled for 4 p.m. And you're not allowed to eat or drink anything after *midnight*.

The night before surgery I could not fall asleep. As a kid I could never fall asleep on Christmas Eve or the night before the first day of school. I'd toss and turn, full of anticipation. This wasn't like that.

I dreaded this surgery that would take an average of four to six hours, naked on a table where your arms are tied down above your head. For the first time since the Dark Days, my legs vibrated again. What could go wrong during six hours of anesthesia? How painful would it be to recover from these amputations? I wanted my breasts gone, but what were the long-term effects of losing this part of my body? I would be completely numb forever and ever. Just like the cancer treadmill I couldn't get off, there was no way around this tortuous, mutilating, and lifesaving surgery.

Suddenly texts and calls were blowing up my phone that something was happening at the nation's capital. It was January 6, 2021, and I couldn't sleep anyway so I turned on the television. I dozed off and on all night, listening to the sights and sounds of an insurrection.

But I woke with clarity. Just like the mornings of my chemotherapy, my subconscious made a decision to embrace what I could not get around. I had to go through this. In fact, this is what I wanted.

I made a last-minute decision to grab photos of my kids. Hungry and thirsty, dressed in my loosest, coziest sweats, I headed to the hospital.

Just as I had bent forward for my epidural during labor, I found myself again cross legged on a hospital bed, preparing for a massive needle to be injected into my spine. The anesthesiologist explained to me that the double mastectomy is slightly different from the epidural: I got two needles into my spine. Top and bottom.

My chest was marked up with two surgeon's markers. My oncology surgeon's marking showing where she would radically remove every ounce of tissue in each breast, and my plastic surgeon's marks where he would replace the tissue with expanders or implants. My plastic surgeon asked my preference here, with direct-to-implants on the same day being a relatively new option for women in my position. But he explained ultimately it would be a game-time decision for him, depending on how my body handled the surgery.

I think of tissue expanders like empty little devices, shaped like breast implants, that your surgeon will fill with saline every few months until it reaches the size you'd like. They feel like plastic in your chest. And they remain there until you go back under anesthesia to exchange them for implants. It was explained to me that this is a good option if you're smaller chested, to stretch out your skin slowly. I can see the benefit here, but I didn't want yet another surgery. I chose direct-to-implants.

Both doctors came to check on me and field any last-minute questions, before I was wheeled back. I had zero questions. Silently, I showed them Greyson and Lilah's photos. They promised to take good care of me and get me home to my children. Somewhere deep inside I believe these were the words I was longing to hear all along.

The anesthesiologist told me it was time.

I bent forward, looking at my kids' faces as the first large needle entered my spine.

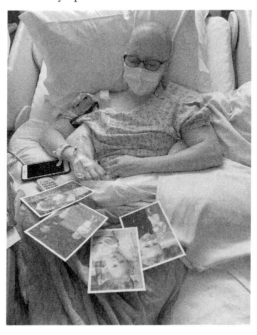

The nurse began to wheel me into the surgery room. I felt panic rising. "Please don't take away these photos until I'm knocked out," I told her.

The hallway was long and dim, but the surgery room was blindingly bright. The anesthesiologist injected something into my IV. Just like the speed of the Benadryl on my first day of chemo, almost instantly I felt this medicine hit me.

To my absolute horror, I told this medical team that I wrote a poem, and I started reciting it.

"Dear Breast Cancer Fighter, you're brave and you're strong."

I don't know how many lines I recited from memory, but I was still looking at my children's faces and that's the last thing I remember before I was out.

I'm a side and stomach sleeper. When I first met with my plastic surgeon there were other decisions that needed to be made, in addition to expanders or implants. Did I want to go flat? Saline or silicone? Same size, smaller, or larger?

I remember appreciating the conversation because all decisions up to that point were not up to me. All medical appointments before that day were tolerable at best, devastating, sickening and scary.

After making those decisions, my plastic surgeon had asked if I had any questions.

"Yes," I said without hesitation. "When can I sleep on my stomach?"

When I woke up from surgery, they told me the blood supply hadn't been strong enough, and I got expanders instead of reconstruction.

I braced to feel disappointment, but it never came. In this moment, still completely numb from my neck to my hips, I couldn't know the physical pain coming my way from a double amputation. I didn't really realize how difficult the recovery would get, being unable to sit up on my own for weeks. I most certainly wasn't prepared for the scars I'd soon see on my chest. I just felt relief that this step was over.

A nurse checked on my bandages, and I told her I could not believe the anesthesia had me reciting my poem. And she said, "You should have seen yourself coming out of it!"

This shocked me since I thought I was currently *in the process* of coming out of it.

"What do you mean?" I asked.

She told me in the surgery room I curled up in a ball so tightly they could not unfurl me. They actually had to take my blood pressure with my leg because they couldn't free an arm. She said I told them I was a side sleeper and would never become a back sleeper no matter what they said. And then I ordered them all out of my bedroom!

Maybe they should write a book about all the crazy things people say under anesthesia.

I don't remember the drive home or the first couple days. It's a blur of agony. A double mastectomy is a lifesaving, yet barbaric surgery. I couldn't sit, stand, or lay without assistance. The pain in my chest, where every last nerve had been severed for life was so deep, it couldn't even be pinpointed. Automatic recliner chairs are often recommended for recovery so you can use the remote to hoist you clear to your feet. The chair was a blessing, because short of sliding to the floor, I was not capable of forward momentum.

Which was how I felt about the recovery all around. Each day I fought for forward momentum.

I slept in the recliner. A travel nurse came to the house every few days to check my progress and four drains. Every few hours my mom had to take two fingers and slowly squeeze the bloody fluid from each drain, into a collection device and record the output for my doctors. Lucky for me, I had one drain right against a nerve. Every time my mom helped me squeeze out the fluid, it zinged a painful, electric jolt up my body.

A couple weeks later, my surgeon pulled the drains, freeing them from me. They left me with two small circular scars on each side of my body. The smallest of many new scars. Under each breast, from one side all the way to the other, were deep scars from my surgery. Above the right breast, a one-inch scar where my port was removed.

Years later, my scars have slightly faded, but they're still very much there. And I've never felt self-conscious of them for even a moment. I even chose a ballgown to a charity event that showed off my port scar. I wore it with pride. They are my battle scars, and I had one hell of a fight.

I recognize that I have come far.

And if anyone knows the medical team from January 2021 who had to take blood pressure from some crazy woman's leg while she was curled up in a tight ball, let them know the joke's on me. I'm still unable to sleep on my stomach!

In Remission

One week after my double mastectomy, I was just barely getting out of the recliner chair when my phone rang. It was a call I had been expecting. I had been waiting for my surgeon to call after my pathology came back from the lab. This is when you find out if the chemotherapy killed all of the cancer cells.

Nervously, I answered the phone. She got straight to the news, saying I had a "complete response" to chemo, which were the words I had prayed so hard to hear. The chemotherapy had 100% eradicated my cancer, which they determine when testing your tissue that's removed after surgery. I cried. I thanked God. I had been holding my breath but in that very exhale, fear of a recurrence began. I didn't even get a moment of peace.

I reluctantly whispered that I was cancer-free to see how that felt, breathing into the universe. I thanked my surgeon and got off the phone and sobbed. The only statistics I knew about triple-negative breast cancer came from the freezing cold doctor's office visit when I was mostly overwhelmed and thinking how I forgot the sweatshirt. But my takeaway that day was pray hard for a complete response to lower your odds of recurrence.

Anxiety began ravaging my days. I felt a heaviness so intense in my chest, I wondered if it was a COVID symptom. I woke in the night gasping, trying to breathe through the fears.

Cancer during a pandemic during a divorce was lonely. I saw so many women in the waiting room and chemo chair with a significant other by their side. I remember sitting across from a couple who looked about my age at the cancer center. They were whispering and laughing as they filled out the weekly questionnaire about our physical and mental state.

The questions asked us on a scale of 1 to 10, to rate our current level of nausea, appetite, fear, etc. Rate our level of concern about sleep, taking medicine, sexual side effects, etc.

As I watched the couple, the man wrapped his arm around the woman's shoulder, and she leaned into him as they laughed. His cheek against the beanie covering her bald head—and suddenly every symptom I had couldn't compare to the yearning I had for affection. Whatever their inside joke was in that moment, it was beautiful to me. And completely out of my reach. After that day, I limited my cancer center people-watching.

I rarely allowed myself a moment's pity party because I knew if I started down that empty road, it would be hard to bounce back.

I entered this cancer marathon on my own. To have and to hold, for better or worse, in sickness and health, I vowed to hold myself up.

But in the days after my surgeon told me I had a complete response, I caught myself experiencing that yearning again. I dreamed of what it would have felt like to have someone wrap me in their arms, to celebrate this win together. To say, "This is what we prayed for together!"

Instead, I prayed for health. I prayed for a chance to watch my children grow.

None of us are prepared for this diagnosis, nor do we have all the tools we want and need. You modify and make it work. I snuggled my babies extra long, extra tight that night at bedtime. I wrapped them in *my* arms.

This is what we'd prayed for together.

THE WAITING ROOM

The first appointment with my oncologist after my double mastectomy was disappointing. After having a complete response to chemo, I entered the waiting room full of hope, bordering on joy. For the first time in more than eight months I felt like I wasn't living in fear.

I had been saying "faith over fear" while waiting for my pathology results to come back. I met a woman at my gym who is a triple-negative survivor and said when she saw her oncologist for the first time post-treatment, they hugged and jumped up and down and she sobbed.

But cancer during COVID meant no hugs across the board, so I lowered my expectations.

Sitting on the exam room table in my pink gown, I was all smiles. The door opened and in walked a young woman I had never met before.

She introduced herself as another oncologist's physician assistant. We made small talk, and she asked if I had a follow-up CT scan because of the lung nodule. Confused, I told her I hadn't and asked if I was supposed to. She chuckled a bit and said yes "because you know how that triple-negative likes to spread."

This single sentence felt like a donkey kick to the face and sent me spiraling. I'd like to say I corrected her, told her that was inappropriate, brushed it off, and walked out. I did nothing but nod my head in disbelief.

During the initial PET scan following my diagnosis, the radiologist discovered a nodule on my lungs and assessed it to be benign. I hadn't thought much about it before this moment, but suddenly my betraying brain was picturing it like a glow-in-the-dark ball attached to my lungs and wreaking havoc in my body.

I started losing sleep. I felt stupid for the joy I experienced walking into that appointment, like I didn't deserve to be strolling around carefree WHEN THERE WAS A LIFE-RUINING, LEECH-LIKE NODULE ATTACHED TO ME.

I felt like that was a good time to google *nodule* because admittedly, I panicked before I had any facts. Definitely not an efficient use of the emotional energy I had learned to so fiercely guard.

A few days later I received a letter in the mail from my insurance company saying the CT scan was DENIED.

They cited my complete response to chemo and said the scan was unnecessary.

At my next doctor's appointment, I was finally able to speak with my oncologist. So much time had passed, the opportunity to celebrate was left in the dust. And now I needed to discuss this nodule. I told her what the PA had said and she appeared surprised, apologizing for the anxiety it had caused, but agreed it would be a good proactive measure to get the scan.

Another month passed and still no insurance approval. I could have filled this book with stories just like this one, from other women whose healthcare was postponed or denied by insurance. But I'm only sharing one. The healthcare I received saved my life and I'm grateful for it, but the system can be maddening, and in many cases, broken. We need to do better.

Finally, my nurse did a peer-to-peer review of my case with the insurance person, and the approval went through. They called me with an authorization number and said I could schedule the chest CT scan.

The scheduler was very kind and patient as she explained the expiration date on my scan had already passed, and she couldn't schedule it. I left a message with my nurse, asking her to resubmit with the correct date and begin waiting again. A week later I tried again to schedule the scan, and this time she said the approval was for pelvis and abdomen but not chest, and she couldn't schedule it.

That really threw me because my basic understanding of anatomy, and the general location of the tiny nodule bomb I'd pictured on my lungs wasn't as close to my pelvis or abdomen as it was to my CHEST.

I finally got full approval for chest, abdomen, and pelvis scan and ran to the bathroom. My body betrayed my relief that it was finally scheduled, with nerves of what it would mean when I got the results. I spent hours sick to my stomach.

One of my best friends joked the scans would be better now that everything was all clear. And I replied that I could finally wear that belly shirt I've been eyeing in my closet.

And then I got back to the toilet.

At my scan appointment I was shaking from nerves. I spent the drive speaking with God, and thanking him for this life, and the future with my children. I told him I knew when I went under the machine that I'd feel a sense of calm knowing He has me in his hands.

Since the beginning of treatment, in and out of doctor's offices all over my town, I've been in a lot of waiting rooms. I've seen a lot of masked faces. I've said hello to a handful of people, but I've never once had a full conversation in a waiting area. Until that day.

After checking in for my CT scan, they put an IV in my arm and gave me two bottles of "iced tea" to drink while I wait. It is my understanding that the drink has a sugary substance in it to make any cancer glow in the body.

I took my cups into the waiting room and nervously began sipping. It was just me and one elderly gentleman sitting there, and my mind was racing. Months of waiting for the test had given me so much anxiety, so many sleepless nights, and now the day had come and I wasn't ready. I was afraid I'd be sick again.

Suddenly the man turned to me and introduced himself as Jerry. Jerry said, "I used to be a singer in a band called the Bell-Aires. We played all around Western Pennsylvania, even opened for a few big acts. I don't know if you've ever heard of us, but maybe some of your family members have. I would sing you a song, but I had a stroke this year and don't have the same voice now. Do you want to sing a song to me?"

I blinked in disbelief. The unexpected kindness threw me! I laughed and told Jerry that I have a terrible voice or else I'd love to sing him a song. And I meant it.

A moment later he smiles and said, "Okay, fine, I'll sing to you."

Quietly, Jerry whispered,

"Maybe I didn't love you

Quite as often as I could"

With more confidence, and a truly beautiful tone, Jerry raised his voice.

"And maybe I didn't treat you

Quite as good as I should have

If I made you feel second best

Girl I'm sorry I was blind

You were always on my mind"

The tears came then. I cried for the life I used to have before cancer, the marriage that I'd lost, the love that was betrayed, the breasts that had betrayed me as well, and I cried from nerves for this damn test that terrified me. I cried and Jerry sang.

I wiped tears from my cheeks and could barely speak. I cleared my throat and said, "Thank you for that song, Jerry. That made my whole day."

Several minutes passed as I quietly sipped my CT-scan tea when Jerry leaned over and said, "I really made your day? Well, thank you. I'm glad to hear it."

Jerry went on to tell me that he was seventy-nine years old, and his mother is a breast cancer survivor—strong and healthy at one-hundred-and-two years old. But sadly he lost his wife to a different cancer a few years prior.

I told Jerry I was so sorry for his loss, and that his mother was a true inspiration. He said he and his wife couldn't have kids, but they adopted a child and sadly drugs took him from them.

There was such sadness in Jerry's eyes.

And then they called him back for his scan.

Just as I finished my second Styrofoam cup of tea, Jerry returned, poking his head back in the waiting room. I looked up expecting him to say goodbye. I was going to thank him again for the song. Instead he said, "Would you and your kids like to get breakfast some day?"

I laughed and said, "Absolutely."

How blessed to have another Godwink when I needed it most. It couldn't be a coincidence that Jerry was placed directly in my path—just the two of us in that waiting room.

I thought about his one-hundred-and-two-year-old cancer-surviving mother. It's a gift to grow old. I felt an inexplicable calm when they called me back for the scan.

A few days later I called up my new friend to tell him my results came back, no signs of cancer anywhere in my chest, abdomen, or pelvis.

"When can you meet for breakfast, Jerry?"

Stolen

One of the biggest blessings I had after my diagnosis was making a "breastie" friend who was one week ahead of me in the process. I always knew what was coming next because Lexi told me.

Lexi is the one who made me laugh until I cried when she thought the radiologist should have at least taken her to dinner before putting a finger in her neck during the port surgery.

Lexi loved to cook and loved being a mom. During treatment, she would FaceTime from her bed, her children snuggled by her side, almost always finding me several states away, also snuggled in bed with my children.

She would always text me, "Hey, girl, hey!"

Lexi was positive, even on our toughest weeks of chemo. I knew what a wig would feel like on my bald head because she bought one right before me. She knew what chemo felt like and talked me through that first treatment and the days that followed. She lost her hair, like clockwork, the week before I did. I knew the shower cry that was coming my way as the hair swirled down the drain because Lexi warned me.

I sent Lexi a few chapters of my book, including the one about pink ribbons. I told her I worried I'd offend people who feel strongly about using pink ribbons as a platform to spread awareness. She immediately reassured me that it was more important to be "raw and honest." She said, "I didn't know I had any strong feelings about pink cups, keychains, or ribbons until it was all smack dab in my face."

We made plans to meet up at a cabin in the middle of nowhere after treatment ended, after seeing a group of breasties ahead of us do it. We'd cook together and finally have a glass of wine that didn't taste like chemo-mouth.

Lexi FaceTimed me as soon as she could sit up, to show off what she called her "Frankenstein scars" under her breasts after her double mastectomy.

It was the last time I saw her because breast cancer is a thief.

Breast cancer is *not* pink ribbons. And it is *not* fair.

I had been waiting to hear back from Lexi for days after she went to the ER. She had told me she wasn't feeling well and that the doctors told her it didn't look good. I was in pure disbelief and told her she would be just fine.

One night my phone dinged with a text as I was putting my daughter to sleep. It was Lexi. I catapulted out of her bed, flying downstairs for privacy, planning to call her immediately. I opened my phone. It was from her husband.

"Cara, this is AJ. It saddens me to tell you that Lexi passed away early this morning."

I wrote this book with the intention of bringing only honesty and positivity to the women diagnosed next. The truth is—breast cancer medical advancements are happening every day. Trials are going on for every facet of this disease. Doctors and researchers are dedicating their lives to finding a cure. There is even a triple-negative vaccine trial underway. *But there is no cure yet.*

Breast cancer is still a monster of an evil disease that does not discriminate. It is taking our friends, sisters, mothers, and wives every day.

Lexi's death sent me spiraling into depression and disbelief. I'm angry and confused that she's not here. That she missed her son's first day of kindergarten. That her children cannot cuddle with her anymore.

I often think about our cabin in the woods, and if I should just go solo. I could cook. I could drink the wine. But it wouldn't be the same without her.

I did make it to a beach eight months after my treatment ended. My body woke me up super early one morning. I padded barefoot into the kitchen to make coffee and sat alone on the balcony in the dark. It was already warm, peaceful, and quiet except for some small waves lapping at the shore. Then a bright orange speck of sun started to peek out from the horizon, emerging from the dark blue water.

I watched the orange slowly grow bigger into the most beautiful sunrise. This was a moment I didn't realize I had been waiting for—through a year of sadness and sickness.

I lifted my mug of coffee and said to the sky, "Hey, girl, hey. You should be here."

BEND WHEN THE WIND BLOWS

L ife after cancer has been an adjustment. Some survivors say it gets easier, month after month, year after year. For a long time, I was waiting for a specific milestone: the day when I didn't think about cancer or fear of a recurrence for a whole day. I reached it and now can go weeks.

I'm back to work and people ask how I'm doing. I always say the same thing, "getting stronger every day." It's not a lie, but it's not quite accurate. I'm getting better at adjusting to this new normal.

When I was a child, I overheard someone say, "You've got to bend when the wind blows." I pictured that in my imagination and liked what I saw, inadvertently adopting it as my life motto for years.

And then faced with a cancer diagnosis, just as I didn't want to run the cancer marathon, I'd have preferred to push back against this wind with all my strength.

I spent a lot of time daydreaming about going back in time and finding my lump before it was stage II. I wanted to go back to my childhood and learn more about my father's side of the family, before being blindsided by this BRCA1 genetic mutation. But you can't change the past.

Turns out I took that motto to heart. I bent with the wind so much, I shared my story and my bald head with tens of thousands of people. Several of my breast cancer posts, according to Facebook, were read by millions of users.

And while it's hard to see those photos I posted, and the pain behind some of my smiles, I don't regret it. I'm grateful for the women it reached and connections I made. Over the last two years some of those strangers on social media have stopped me in stores, restaurants, and when I'm out on stories for work to say they prayed for me. A woman at the airport shouted that she's prayed for me every single night, and after reading in the paper that I was in remission, she'd decided to keep me in her nighttime prayers. A woman in line at Panera burst in to tears and asked if she could give me a hug.

You see people commonly throw out, "thanks for the prayers!" But I am thankful with all my heart, for all those prayers. In fact, I think about it often. I'll never figure out how to thank everyone enough.

When I sat down to write this chapter I googled "you've got to bend when the wind blows," and to my surprise, nothing really came up. I will never even remember who said it to me.

Instead that Google search brought up a different quote about wind, and it felt even more powerful. In fact, I love it so much I might swap out life mottos for this one:

"She stood in the storm, and when the wind did not blow her way, she adjusted her sails."

The spring after my reconstructive surgery, I was getting ready for work and put on a plain black dress. My daughter had been sitting on my bedroom floor, watching me get ready.

While I was looking for a necklace, Lilah said she had one for me in her bedroom, and her little legs sent her flying. She came back in with two silver *bracelets* that must have been sent as gifts during treatment. She said she would wear one, and I could wear the other. We sat down on my bedroom floor together.

She took a moment to look at each bracelet and gave me one. I thanked her and began to read what was engraved on the inside. It's a bracelet I have no memory of receiving, owning, or even seeing before that moment. And it said:

"She stood in the storm, and when the wind did not blow her way, she adjusted her sails."

Putting on the bracelet, I almost left for work. I had been back on-air reporting in my beautiful wig for a few weeks now. I pulled the wig off and secured it back on the mannequin head on my dresser.

It felt like time to show our viewers, and anyone who had ever battled cancer, that I had about two inches of hair on my head and was proud to show it.

Lilah smiled at me and said, "Verwy pwetty."

It felt good to adjust my sails.

Muscle Memory

S hower after shower, I enjoyed the sensation of shampooing a little more hair every week after chemo ended. The buzz cut fuzzy sensation was fun. I appreciated squeezing water with two fingers from the mini mullet forming behind my ears. I catalogued the hair growth because it was part of the forward momentum that I had longed for, after racking up so much loss. Each time I noticed substantial hair growth while shampooing, though, I was reminded of something fascinating I'd experienced during chemo. Despite being acutely aware that I'd lost my hair, almost every time I took a shower, I forgot I was bald.

I believe it's a muscle memory thing, but I startled each time I went to wash my hair and it just wasn't there.

My hands would automatically reach up; my fingers automatically spread open like I'd done thousands of times before when wetting my hair. It would happen fast and let me down every time.

It reminds me of this: I've been reading books before bed for as long as I can remember—wearing glasses. As far back as fifth grade, with just my glasses and a flashlight under the covers, I really began to love reading books before falling asleep. Eventually I didn't have to hide this from my mom and came out from under there to escape into a book before bed every night. It's always been one of my favorite ways to wind down. When I was twenty-five years old, I got Lasik eye surgery. The first night I read in bed with my newly fixed eyesight, I got sleepy and reached to take off the glasses. I laughed in pure surprise as my hand hit my nose. No glasses there! And I was shocked that it wasn't a one-time incident. For months, I sleepily reached to take off my glasses and hit myself in the nose!

And then one day I remembered I don't wear glasses anymore, and just rolled over and went to sleep.

Just like the glasses, with only a few chemo treatments left, I finally stopped forgetting I didn't have hair in the shower. I finally stopped threading my fingers and deflating when they didn't find hair there. To clean a bald head, I just swiped some shampoo in a circle and rinsed it away. Showers had never been so fast. And then hair started to grow again.

It's just hair, people may think. But you don't have to minimize how harrowing it is to suddenly lose your hair within weeks of a cancer diagnosis turning your world upside down. None of us are ready for it.

But I urged myself not to adjust fully to this foreign, excruciating period.

Some of us are coming through this with scars for life. I've accepted this. My scars are evidence of the battle I fought. But I was counting on my muscle memory to help me bounce back.

I'll never forget the day my hair fit into a full ponytail for the first time since losing it all. I noticed it, of course, while washing out my shampoo in the shower. I gathered up the now ultra-curly, thick bob-length hair in shock that no wisps were falling forward.

I wrapped myself in a towel, grabbed a hair tie, and let my fingers effortlessly remember how to wrap it around my fist, loop it over, and pull the hair out. I smiled into the bathroom mirror that has reflected a great deal of sadness. I smiled at my cute, Troll-like puff of hair up there. I could never forget how to do this.

THE FLOWER

B uilding back confidence after cancer has been one of the steeper hills in this seemingly never-ending marathon.

You want to race downhill to that finish line, while outside forces keep moving the cones.

But therapy has been helpful.

While you're doing all the work to get your physical strength back, talking through the emotional pain that comes with a cancer diagnosis has been critical through my recovery.

Throughout chemotherapy, I propped my pillow up on my bed, placed my laptop across from me for weekly Zoom therapy sessions. My therapist was the first person to so eloquently state "that which did not serve me on my quest to live stress-free could be let go."

She gave me this pass to apply that to all areas of my life---and I'm still letting go on a grand scale. I'm an Oprah: you get let go! You get let go! I'm also a Marie Kondo: you don't bring me joy! You get tossed out.

Marie Kondo, the cleaning guru on Netflix, tells people who are working to organize and tidy their homes, if an object doesn't bring you joy, don't try to justify its place in your house. Just say thank you, get rid of it and move on.

Cleaning the post-cancer life house has been a mixed bag of letting go of everything that doesn't bring me joy and anything and anyone who causes me stress.   But also pulling close what brings happiness, peace and health. And moving on.

To continue working on my mental health after chemo ended, I needed some more therapy.

By this time, the post-pandemic world opened up in-person appointments, and I was out the door. I wanted to sit across from a therapist, face to face, and let it all out.

I skipped into that office filled with embarrassing levels of joy. I was just happy to be there.

"Tell me about yourself. What brings you here? What do you want to work through," my new therapist asked.

The giant smile on my face lasted only moments before I fully broke down. Where did I even begin? Barely pausing to take a breath, I let it all out. "I separated from my husband right as the pandemic hit and we were stuck living together and nothing was open and I was probably clinically depressed and I've always been too nice and then I found a lump on my breast and I was diagnosed with triple-negative breast cancer and it's one of the most aggressive forms and my breasts were just amputated and I'm living in fear and I'm a shell of my former self and I've always been a people pleaser and it's hard to look in the mirror and hard to share custody and I feel unwanted and unloved and my childhood was lonely."

I reached for the Kleenex.

"So just some minor issues, then?" she asked.

She didn't really ask that. Professional and poised, she just suggested we start with the marriage that day and could tackle the rest from there.

Each week I was skipping into therapy with that smile on my face, always grateful for post pandemic appointments to be in-person. I wanted connection so badly, even with a therapist. I was happy to be doing the work. I wanted to heal. But each week, I got a few minutes into our session before I broke down.

My pre-cancer lighthearted demeanor had been overshadowed by so much darkness. I was spending my days serving the peanuts to my children, my medical team, my family and colleagues. And I swallowed the pain. In an effort to never let them see you cry, my tears dried up, and I became numb. It's hard to find joy when some days you feel nothing.

I admitted to something that had taken one of the biggest beatings, but I was embarrassed to speak it out loud: my self-confidence.

I didn't enter marriage expecting to be divorced. I didn't approach 40 expecting to be bald and single. I had repeated my mantra about breast cancer being ugly one too many times. I didn't want cancer to define me, but I was inadvertently defining myself. It felt a little cruel of me.

My therapist convinced me to go on a few dates, which was terrifying but also a nice distraction. I couldn't wait to share those stories with her. I told her about the guy who said something outlandishly ridiculous about politics on a first date. I looked at him and then looked at the railing next to us and said, "excuse me while I just fling myself over this balcony."

"Look how far you've come! You're not the too-nice people pleaser anymore," my therapist said.

Solid point. I swelled a little with pride.

She pointed out that I was out there living again, back to being just a mom like I had dreamed and longed for so deeply. I was waking every morning before my kids, typing away at a book in hopes of helping other women. I was walking into therapy with my head held high now, with conviction that I would not let my diagnosis define me.

I thanked her for these kind words, allowing myself to soak them in.

Did I believe her or was I just serving myself the peanuts?

She said she knew that my confidence still needed to be built back up, and like everything else on this marathon, it would take time.

"But would it be okay to tell you how I see you, which is much different than you see yourself?" she asked.

"Yes, of course. How do you see me?"

It's a description that rendered me speechless, with tears streaming down my face. And I think many of us breast cancer survivors, who want to shake off the labels, may appreciate this one.

"You're the flower, blooming through the concrete."

Resilience

There's an unspoken expectation that we are going to finish treatment and bounce right back. We are tethered to our Chemo Chairs for months and months and then just tossed back into the world like a deer on ice trying to land on our feet.

Nobody craves normalcy more than us! If only it were so simple and easy to move forward, tossing a match behind you and burning the whole ugly experience to the ground.

Burn the pink tchotchkes while you're at it.

Survivors are forced to figure it out as we go, how to move on after being altered catastrophically. How to find a new normal. How to be resilient after taking such a hard blow.

The definition of *resilience* is the ability to withstand or adjust to challenges—or the ability for something to return to its original shape after it has been altered.

We are altered: with scars across our chests, under our reconstructed breasts, on the sides of our bodies, and in our hearts. Thank God we have a tribe of women who understand what this feels like because without those connections, we might go mad from trying to explain to people the madness that is a breast cancer diagnosis.

I had wondered if I'd find resilience came a little easier when my hair grew back simply because I wouldn't have that daily reminder of loss when looking in the mirror. But

I accepted that for the rest of my life, my scars—as much as I wasn't embarrassed by them—would be a reminder every time I stepped out of the shower.

And still, if you could magically remove those scars, I'd have trouble moving forward because I haven't begun to heal the scars on my heart— after this disease took a friend.

Breast cancer stole Lexi from this world like a thief that I don't know how to punish.

As survivors, we don't know how to mourn the loss of someone we cared about, someone who shared our pain and sorrows and frankly, could have been us.

I am both a shell of my former self, while also a stronger version.

Some of that strength was mustered up from finding purpose through the pain. It was a cathartic experience to jot down the details of how this disease affected me week by week. Many cancer survivors who have gained that unexpected, newfound mental fortitude go on to achieve greatness. Charities are created, money is raised, awareness is made, groups are formed, races are run, stories are celebrated.

Other survivors want to close the door on their "journey" and simply move on. It's tempting to lock the bolt and latch the door— put a few barricade blocks there for good measure and never look back.

No judgement zone here. You get to take your losses, your lessons, your wins and your strength and take your life back, however you see fit.

I do hope you shower yourself with compassion. And give yourself grace and time to heal. Healing is cumulative but being *healed* might be an unattainable goal for us all. It's okay to be a work in progress, striving to heal more as time passes. I'd like to be flexible and honest with my delicate post-cancer state of mind. *Today was a good day, let's pray for some more,* I tell my mind.

I now try to live life with faith over fear. I have pulled myself out of the fetal position and child's pose. First, I crawled and now I stand, and I am beginning to walk with that faith every day.

But that would have to include the days I feel an ache, or a pain and my heart starts to race, and I feel my knees going weak. Occasionally I still feel myself headed back to the floor.

How many years out until I can feel these moments and let them go, without an ounce of panic?

Maybe the answer is never. That carefreeness is one of the many things cancer stole from me, and I don't think I'll ever get it back.

But I always tell women: "You are more than this fight."

Instead of desperately trying to heal, I am trying to re-member who I was. I am a mother first. A daughter. A friend. A storyteller. Who are you? Here's your pass to find her again.

Survivors get a second chance to really appreciate life's little moments: the day-to-day mundane stuff that we used take for granted— a cliche, but simply true. I'm soaking it all in. I'm feeling every damn joy, big or small, that comes my way. I am sipping my coffee that doesn't taste like vinegar with such appreciation every morning, it borders on jubilance!

If the challenge is moving forward, maybe we do that by going back. Take note of the moments and days you feel like your old self again.

For me, this is resilience: catching myself being myself again, and thanking God for it. Because I am more than this fight.

Life After Loss

I spent so much time explaining the Dark Days because I know that's where a lot of women will be residing when they open this book. It's when you could use a friend who has been there before.

The friendships I made in the summer of 2020 with the women who recently finished chemotherapy will forever hold a spot in my heart. They answered endless questions and provided immeasurable hope simply from showing me what life could look like after treatment. They showed me a path forward.

The friendships I made with women in the breast cancer community have been some of the most meaningful in my life.

I ended up going to brunch with Gina, as planned. We decided to make it a monthly tradition and went almost every month for the last two years. Together we threw out our wigs, we took selfies at restaurants which captured our hair growing longer, our friendship growing along the way. We talked about what we lost, what we learned, what we feared and what no one else understood. We realized one day, after two years, that we no longer talked almost exclusively about cancer.

Something beautiful snuck up on us in the process of healing. We weren't just dreaming of the next chapter of our lives, we were living it.

I had so much hair on my head last year, I looked like a hedgehog. My curls are now crazy and thick, and grew so fast I passed the pixie and went straight to a mullet. I recently chopped the mullet and have just normal shoulder length hair. Where there was once smoothness, stubble, and patches, there is a now whole Chia Pet.

My eyelashes and brows returned quickly. I heard through the Facebook cancer group grapevine that your lashes almost always go through three cycles before they stay for good. Just like I wondered if I'd be the one person who didn't lose her hair on my treatment regimen, or didn't experience chemo nausea, or didn't have to have her chest carved open for a port, or didn't experience the peeing your pants sensation during a PET scan, I also wondered if maybe I'd get lucky enough to lose the lashes just once or twice.

But about seven months out from treatment, I lost the damn lashes again for round three. Except this time the outermost lashes remained. It looked like someone glued the small, thin strips just to the edges of my eyes. If only I hadn't chucked those magnetic lashes into the trash after my photo shoot—I could have evened them out nicely by wearing them the wrong way again.

My short-term memory has slowly returned. I doubt it will ever be the same. Chemo brain and fog turned out to be one of the most challenging obstacles. Maybe I'm grateful, though, to forget some of it.

December 2020

My children have surprised me with what they remember about their mom's days fighting breast cancer. They remember the cuddles, the bald head and ringing those bells. They've never once mentioned remembering me with my head in the toilet; I hope I shielded them from the ugliest days.

They also remember praying.

These days, my son's nighttime prayers vary but often include moms with breast cancer. His little brain has also added 'help for the homeless' and 'making bullies become nice'. He recently helped me teach my daughter The Lord's Prayer, and her sweet little voice now recites that with us. "Anything else you want to add? Anyone you want to pray for?" I asked her the other night.

"I pray for myself," she said smiling. *Goodnight!* We all laughed and laughed! I feel like the luckiest mom.

Recently, my kids and I were ordering food at a restaurant and a boy from my son's kindergarten class approached our table and said hello. "I heard you and Greyson's dad broke up!" he announced loudly.

Caught off guard, I chuckled and told him that he'd heard correctly. Before I could add anything else he continued. "Yeah, I hear you are now just friends and you are nice to each other."

My son smiled proudly at me, confident in what he'd shared with his school friend. I text my ex-husband about the exchange, relieved more than anything that we were getting this right.

December 2022 - Danielle Nichole
Photography

Physically I am stronger. I'm back to kickboxing and find I can zone out, similar to yoga, and punch with a vengeance. I could punch anything or anyone, but I've let that anger go. These punches are exclusively to strengthen my body. I'm fighting-ready for this chapter of my life.

Before boxers put on boxing gloves, you have to wrap your hands to protect the knuckles. One day last month I stood in the gym, wrapping my hands with a lump in my throat, trying not to cry. That morning, someone had asked me when was my "cancer-versary".

I had heard this term in breast cancer circles but really didn't know what it meant. Was it the day I felt my lump, the day of diagnosis, the day I finished treatment? I hesitated to google because you never know what could pop up. But I did the search and found out the cancer-versary is "a milestone defined by you." It could be any of those things.

I opened my iPhone calendar and swiped back through the months, past this spring of recovery, and winter of reconstruction, past the fall of chemotherapy, and the summer of Dark Days to the weeks after I found the lump. I didn't have anything in the calendar like "diagnosed with triple-negative." In fact, my first diagnosis was wrong, so does that even count? Those calendar entries were chock full of doctor appointments and scans. A blur now, but rushing back to me nonetheless. I looked at today's date and cross-referenced it in the calendar. It was the day I had started chemotherapy. My jaw dropped. "Goes so slow as it flies right by," I whispered.

I finished wrapping my hands and pulled on my pink-but-not-breast-cancer-pink boxing gloves, using my teeth to tighten the Velcro strap. The bell dinged, and I landed my first punch on the bag. And then another and another, giving it my all. When the bell rang again, I used my forearm to wipe tears that slipped down my face. I paused to glance in the mirror, gloves on my hips. And finally, *finally* said it to my reflection.

"You're a fighter."

If you were recently diagnosed with breast cancer, in the thick of it, or in the healing stages, remember this: On your hardest day, and in your darkest hour, we are with you. A tribe of women who have crawled through it.

You are not alone.

Make plans and get fighting-ready for the next chapter.

Take it from me, a flower blooming from the concrete after the breast year of my life.

Epilogue: Light After Dark

Dear Greyson and Lilah,

Tomorrow is my last chemo. I can say for sure chemotherapy is the most difficult, painful experience of my life. But these months recovering at home, quarantined from the world because of Covid, I will cherish because of all the time with you. When I look through my photos on my phone, I can't believe all the smiles and cuddles. We really made the most out of a horrible situation. We had more good days than bad— by far. Watching you two form a friendship and play and laugh together in front of me is priceless. I'm trying to count my blessings and look for the good. You two are the greatest blessings of all time. To me, you're the good.

You're everything I prayed my children would turn out to be. Your kind hearts kept me going on the hardest days.

The best part of tomorrow's final chemo, is it marks the beginning of a new chapter, where I just get to be a mom again. Not a mom going through cancer treatment. I kept thinking each week that passed that maybe this would be the week you complained or acted out, but you never did. You are pure joy and I'm the luckiest mom in the world.

Before chemo started I emailed you guys and I looked back to see what I wrote. Greyson, you told me 'there is light after dark'.

You two were the light during my darkest dark.

Love,

Mom

Dear Greyson and Lilah,

I might get some difficult news today and I wanted to write to you before I'm too overwhelmed with doctors and plans and fears.

Last night you asked me to lay in bed with you, G. We were cuddling and you said, You know mommy there is light after dark?

I had to choke back tears, but honestly it was exactly what I needed to hear. And then you said, Luke Combs said so. And you started singing his new song. And I laughed.

2.5 weeks ago I felt a lump on my breast and we already know it's cancer. We don't know how scary it is or what kind of treatment the doctors will need to do to help make me better.

I broke this news on social media and I've been really humbled and appreciative of prayers from thousands and thousands of strangers.

But listen, none of them and nothing else matters in this journey except you two.

I hear that I'll need to be strong and fight.

Nothing could make me fight harder and stronger than you two.

My fear in this journey is they'll say I need chemotherapy and it may make me sick or extremely tired, and I don't want that to affect you. I hope to shelter you from as much as this process as possible. One of the possible procedures is to completely remove both boobs, which I have told the doctors, "take em!" They can have my boobs. I only want my life with my babies. If I have that procedure you guys won't be able to tackle me or even hug me for about a month. This is going to be hard because you tackle me every single day. Dozens of hugs a day. Some days you two fight over who gets to tackle me and love on me, and sometimes you share. I have two arms and they can cuddle perfectly with you both. It's these two boobs I don't need and pray that God just lets the doctors take them and heals me.

I'll know a lot more about my diagnosis today. I know whatever they tell me I'll be able to handle because I am doing it for you.

I love you more than anything in the entire world.

To the moon and back,

Mommy

Printed in Great Britain
by Amazon